False garlic and Engelmann's hedgehog
LARRY ULRICH

Another product from
Arizona Highways magazine, a monthly publication
of the Arizona Department of Transportation.
Copyright ©1996 by the Department of Transportation,
State of Arizona. Second printing, 1999.

ISBN 0-916179-94-X

Arizona Highways
2039 West Lewis Avenue
Phoenix, Arizona 85009
(602) 258-6641
www.arizhwys.com

PUBLISHER
Nina M. La France

DESIGN
Patricia Romano

COVER DESIGN
Ronda Johnson-Freeman

PRODUCTION DIRECTOR
Cindy Mackey

DIRECTOR OF PHOTOGRAPHY
Peter Ensenberger

PHOTO EDITOR
Scott Condray

PHOTOGRAPHY
Arizona Highways Contributors

COVER PHOTOGRAPH
Saguaro forest, Cabeza Prieta National Wildlife Refuge
RANDY PRENTICE

		HOLIDAY GREETINGS		
		Year	Sent	Rec

NAME _____

ADDRESS _____

CITY/STATE/ZIP _____

HOME _____ OFFICE _____

E-MAIL _____ FAX _____

		HOLIDAY GREETINGS		
		Year	Sent	Rec

NAME _____

ADDRESS _____

CITY/STATE/ZIP _____

HOME _____ OFFICE _____

E-MAIL _____ FAX _____

		HOLIDAY GREETINGS		
		Year	Sent	Rec

NAME _____

ADDRESS _____

CITY/STATE/ZIP _____

HOME _____ OFFICE _____

E-MAIL _____ FAX _____

		HOLIDAY GREETINGS		
		Year	Sent	Rec

NAME _____

ADDRESS _____

CITY/STATE/ZIP _____

HOME _____ OFFICE _____

E-MAIL _____ FAX _____

		HOLIDAY GREETINGS		
		Year	Sent	Rec

NAME _____

ADDRESS _____

CITY/STATE/ZIP _____

HOME _____ OFFICE _____

E-MAIL _____ FAX _____

NAME _____

ADDRESS _____

CITY/STATE/ZIP _____

HOME _____OFFICE _____

E-MAIL _____FAX _____

HOLIDAY GREETINGS		
Year	Sent	Rec

NAME _____

ADDRESS _____

CITY/STATE/ZIP _____

HOME _____OFFICE _____

E-MAIL _____FAX _____

HOLIDAY GREETINGS		
Year	Sent	Rec

NAME _____

ADDRESS _____

CITY/STATE/ZIP _____

HOME _____OFFICE _____

E-MAIL _____FAX _____

HOLIDAY GREETINGS		
Year	Sent	Rec

NAME _____

ADDRESS _____

CITY/STATE/ZIP _____

HOME _____OFFICE _____

E-MAIL _____FAX _____

HOLIDAY GREETINGS		
Year	Sent	Rec

NAME _____

ADDRESS _____

CITY/STATE/ZIP _____

HOME _____OFFICE _____

E-MAIL _____FAX _____

HOLIDAY GREETINGS		
Year	Sent	Rec

NAME _____

ADDRESS _____

CITY/STATE/ZIP _____

HOME _____ OFFICE _____

E-MAIL _____ FAX _____

HOLIDAY GREETINGS		
Year	Sent	Rec

NAME _____

ADDRESS _____

CITY/STATE/ZIP _____

HOME _____ OFFICE _____

E-MAIL _____ FAX _____

HOLIDAY GREETINGS		
Year	Sent	Rec

NAME _____

ADDRESS _____

CITY/STATE/ZIP _____

HOME _____ OFFICE _____

E-MAIL _____ FAX _____

HOLIDAY GREETINGS		
Year	Sent	Rec

NAME _____

ADDRESS _____

CITY/STATE/ZIP _____

HOME _____ OFFICE _____

E-MAIL _____ FAX _____

HOLIDAY GREETINGS		
Year	Sent	Rec

NAME _____

ADDRESS _____

CITY/STATE/ZIP _____

HOME _____ OFFICE _____

E-MAIL _____ FAX _____

HOLIDAY GREETINGS		
Year	Sent	Rec

NAME _____

HOLIDAY GREETINGS		
Year	Sent	Rec

ADDRESS _____

CITY/STATE/ZIP _____

HOME _____OFFICE _____

E-MAIL _____FAX _____

NAME _____

HOLIDAY GREETINGS		
Year	Sent	Rec

ADDRESS _____

CITY/STATE/ZIP _____

HOME _____OFFICE _____

E-MAIL _____FAX _____

NAME _____

HOLIDAY GREETINGS		
Year	Sent	Rec

ADDRESS _____

CITY/STATE/ZIP _____

HOME _____OFFICE _____

E-MAIL _____FAX _____

NAME _____

HOLIDAY GREETINGS		
Year	Sent	Rec

ADDRESS _____

CITY/STATE/ZIP _____

HOME _____OFFICE _____

E-MAIL _____FAX _____

NAME _____

HOLIDAY GREETINGS		
Year	Sent	Rec

ADDRESS _____

CITY/STATE/ZIP _____

HOME _____OFFICE _____

E-MAIL _____FAX _____

NAME _____

ADDRESS _____

CITY/STATE/ZIP _____

HOME _____ OFFICE _____

E-MAIL _____ FAX _____

HOLIDAY GREETINGS		
Year	Sent	Rec

NAME _____

ADDRESS _____

CITY/STATE/ZIP _____

HOME _____ OFFICE _____

E-MAIL _____ FAX _____

HOLIDAY GREETINGS		
Year	Sent	Rec

NAME _____

ADDRESS _____

CITY/STATE/ZIP _____

HOME _____ OFFICE _____

E-MAIL _____ FAX _____

HOLIDAY GREETINGS		
Year	Sent	Rec

NAME _____

ADDRESS _____

CITY/STATE/ZIP _____

HOME _____ OFFICE _____

E-MAIL _____ FAX _____

HOLIDAY GREETINGS		
Year	Sent	Rec

NAME _____

ADDRESS _____

CITY/STATE/ZIP _____

HOME _____ OFFICE _____

E-MAIL _____ FAX _____

HOLIDAY GREETINGS		
Year	Sent	Rec

	HOLIDAY GREETINGS		
	Year	Sent	Rec

NAME _____

ADDRESS _____

CITY/STATE/ZIP _____

HOME _____OFFICE _____

E-MAIL _____FAX _____

	HOLIDAY GREETINGS		
	Year	Sent	Rec

NAME _____

ADDRESS _____

CITY/STATE/ZIP _____

HOME _____OFFICE _____

E-MAIL _____FAX _____

	HOLIDAY GREETINGS		
	Year	Sent	Rec

NAME _____

ADDRESS _____

CITY/STATE/ZIP _____

HOME _____OFFICE _____

E-MAIL _____FAX _____

	HOLIDAY GREETINGS		
	Year	Sent	Rec

NAME _____

ADDRESS _____

CITY/STATE/ZIP _____

HOME _____OFFICE _____

E-MAIL _____FAX _____

	HOLIDAY GREETINGS		
	Year	Sent	Rec

NAME _____

ADDRESS _____

CITY/STATE/ZIP _____

HOME _____OFFICE _____

E-MAIL _____FAX _____

Sand dunes near Yuma
ROBERT MCDONALD

NAME		
ADDRESS		
CITY/STATE/ZIP		
HOME	OFFICE	
E-MAIL	FAX	

HOLIDAY GREETINGS

Year	Sent	Rec

NAME		
ADDRESS		
CITY/STATE/ZIP		
HOME	OFFICE	
E-MAIL	FAX	

HOLIDAY GREETINGS

Year	Sent	Rec

NAME		
ADDRESS		
CITY/STATE/ZIP		
HOME	OFFICE	
E-MAIL	FAX	

HOLIDAY GREETINGS

Year	Sent	Rec

NAME		
ADDRESS		
CITY/STATE/ZIP		
HOME	OFFICE	
E-MAIL	FAX	

HOLIDAY GREETINGS

Year	Sent	Rec

NAME		
ADDRESS		
CITY/STATE/ZIP		
HOME	OFFICE	
E-MAIL	FAX	

HOLIDAY GREETINGS

Year	Sent	Rec

NAME _____

ADDRESS _____

CITY/STATE/ZIP _____

HOME _____ OFFICE _____

E-MAIL _____ FAX _____

HOLIDAY GREETINGS		
Year	Sent	Rec

NAME _____

ADDRESS _____

CITY/STATE/ZIP _____

HOME _____ OFFICE _____

E-MAIL _____ FAX _____

HOLIDAY GREETINGS		
Year	Sent	Rec

NAME _____

ADDRESS _____

CITY/STATE/ZIP _____

HOME _____ OFFICE _____

E-MAIL _____ FAX _____

HOLIDAY GREETINGS		
Year	Sent	Rec

NAME _____

ADDRESS _____

CITY/STATE/ZIP _____

HOME _____ OFFICE _____

E-MAIL _____ FAX _____

HOLIDAY GREETINGS		
Year	Sent	Rec

NAME _____

ADDRESS _____

CITY/STATE/ZIP _____

HOME _____ OFFICE _____

E-MAIL _____ FAX _____

HOLIDAY GREETINGS		
Year	Sent	Rec

NAME _____	HOLIDAY GREETINGS		
	Year	Sent	Rec
ADDRESS _____			
CITY/STATE/ZIP _____			
HOME _____OFFICE _____			
E-MAIL _____FAX _____			

NAME _____	HOLIDAY GREETINGS		
	Year	Sent	Rec
ADDRESS _____			
CITY/STATE/ZIP _____			
HOME _____OFFICE _____			
E-MAIL _____FAX _____			

NAME _____	HOLIDAY GREETINGS		
	Year	Sent	Rec
ADDRESS _____			
CITY/STATE/ZIP _____			
HOME _____OFFICE _____			
E-MAIL _____FAX _____			

NAME _____	HOLIDAY GREETINGS		
	Year	Sent	Rec
ADDRESS _____			
CITY/STATE/ZIP _____			
HOME _____OFFICE _____			
E-MAIL _____FAX _____			

NAME _____	HOLIDAY GREETINGS		
	Year	Sent	Rec
ADDRESS _____			
CITY/STATE/ZIP _____			
HOME _____OFFICE _____			
E-MAIL _____FAX _____			

NAME _____	HOLIDAY GREETINGS		
	Year	Sent	Rec
ADDRESS _____			
CITY/STATE/ZIP _____			
HOME _____ OFFICE _____			
E-MAIL _____ FAX _____			

NAME _____	HOLIDAY GREETINGS		
	Year	Sent	Rec
ADDRESS _____			
CITY/STATE/ZIP _____			
HOME _____ OFFICE _____			
E-MAIL _____ FAX _____			

NAME _____	HOLIDAY GREETINGS		
	Year	Sent	Rec
ADDRESS _____			
CITY/STATE/ZIP _____			
HOME _____ OFFICE _____			
E-MAIL _____ FAX _____			

NAME _____	HOLIDAY GREETINGS		
	Year	Sent	Rec
ADDRESS _____			
CITY/STATE/ZIP _____			
HOME _____ OFFICE _____			
E-MAIL _____ FAX _____			

NAME _____	HOLIDAY GREETINGS		
	Year	Sent	Rec
ADDRESS _____			
CITY/STATE/ZIP _____			
HOME _____ OFFICE _____			
E-MAIL _____ FAX _____			

	HOLIDAY GREETINGS		
	Year	Sent	Rec

NAME _____

ADDRESS _____

CITY/STATE/ZIP _____

HOME _____ OFFICE _____

E-MAIL _____ FAX _____

	HOLIDAY GREETINGS		
	Year	Sent	Rec

NAME _____

ADDRESS _____

CITY/STATE/ZIP _____

HOME _____ OFFICE _____

E-MAIL _____ FAX _____

	HOLIDAY GREETINGS		
	Year	Sent	Rec

NAME _____

ADDRESS _____

CITY/STATE/ZIP _____

HOME _____ OFFICE _____

E-MAIL _____ FAX _____

	HOLIDAY GREETINGS		
	Year	Sent	Rec

NAME _____

ADDRESS _____

CITY/STATE/ZIP _____

HOME _____ OFFICE _____

E-MAIL _____ FAX _____

	HOLIDAY GREETINGS		
	Year	Sent	Rec

NAME _____

ADDRESS _____

CITY/STATE/ZIP _____

HOME _____ OFFICE _____

E-MAIL _____ FAX _____

NAME _____	HOLIDAY GREETINGS		
	Year	Sent	Rec
ADDRESS _____			
CITY/STATE/ZIP _____			
HOME _____OFFICE _____			
E-MAIL _____FAX _____			

NAME _____	HOLIDAY GREETINGS		
	Year	Sent	Rec
ADDRESS _____			
CITY/STATE/ZIP _____			
HOME _____OFFICE _____			
E-MAIL _____FAX _____			

NAME _____	HOLIDAY GREETINGS		
	Year	Sent	Rec
ADDRESS _____			
CITY/STATE/ZIP _____			
HOME _____OFFICE _____			
E-MAIL _____FAX _____			

NAME _____	HOLIDAY GREETINGS		
	Year	Sent	Rec
ADDRESS _____			
CITY/STATE/ZIP _____			
HOME _____OFFICE _____			
E-MAIL _____FAX _____			

NAME _____	HOLIDAY GREETINGS		
	Year	Sent	Rec
ADDRESS _____			
CITY/STATE/ZIP _____			
HOME _____OFFICE _____			
E-MAIL _____FAX _____			

New Mexican locust and quaking aspens
JACK DYKINGA

NAME _____

ADDRESS _____

CITY/STATE/ZIP _____

HOME _____ OFFICE _____

E-MAIL _____ FAX _____

NAME _____

ADDRESS _____

CITY/STATE/ZIP _____

HOME _____ OFFICE _____

E-MAIL _____ FAX _____

NAME _____

ADDRESS _____

CITY/STATE/ZIP _____

HOME _____ OFFICE _____

E-MAIL _____ FAX _____

NAME _____

ADDRESS _____

CITY/STATE/ZIP _____

HOME _____ OFFICE _____

E-MAIL _____ FAX _____

NAME _____

ADDRESS _____

CITY/STATE/ZIP _____

HOME _____ OFFICE _____

E-MAIL _____ FAX _____

NAME _____

ADDRESS _____

CITY/STATE/ZIP _____

HOME _____ OFFICE _____

E-MAIL _____ FAX _____

HOLIDAY GREETINGS		
Year	Sent	Rec

NAME _____

ADDRESS _____

CITY/STATE/ZIP _____

HOME _____ OFFICE _____

E-MAIL _____ FAX _____

HOLIDAY GREETINGS		
Year	Sent	Rec

NAME _____

ADDRESS _____

CITY/STATE/ZIP _____

HOME _____ OFFICE _____

E-MAIL _____ FAX _____

HOLIDAY GREETINGS		
Year	Sent	Rec

NAME _____

ADDRESS _____

CITY/STATE/ZIP _____

HOME _____ OFFICE _____

E-MAIL _____ FAX _____

HOLIDAY GREETINGS		
Year	Sent	Rec

NAME _____

ADDRESS _____

CITY/STATE/ZIP _____

HOME _____ OFFICE _____

E-MAIL _____ FAX _____

HOLIDAY GREETINGS		
Year	Sent	Rec

NAME	HOLIDAY GREETINGS		
	Year	Sent	Rec
ADDRESS			
CITY/STATE/ZIP			
HOME _____ OFFICE _____			
E-MAIL _____ FAX _____			

NAME	HOLIDAY GREETINGS		
	Year	Sent	Rec
ADDRESS			
CITY/STATE/ZIP			
HOME _____ OFFICE _____			
E-MAIL _____ FAX _____			

NAME	HOLIDAY GREETINGS		
	Year	Sent	Rec
ADDRESS			
CITY/STATE/ZIP			
HOME _____ OFFICE _____			
E-MAIL _____ FAX _____			

NAME	HOLIDAY GREETINGS		
	Year	Sent	Rec
ADDRESS			
CITY/STATE/ZIP			
HOME _____ OFFICE _____			
E-MAIL _____ FAX _____			

NAME	HOLIDAY GREETINGS		
	Year	Sent	Rec
ADDRESS			
CITY/STATE/ZIP			
HOME _____ OFFICE _____			
E-MAIL _____ FAX _____			

NAME _____

ADDRESS _____

CITY/STATE/ZIP _____

HOME _____OFFICE _____

E-MAIL _____FAX _____

HOLIDAY GREETINGS		
Year	Sent	Rec

NAME _____

ADDRESS _____

CITY/STATE/ZIP _____

HOME _____OFFICE _____

E-MAIL _____FAX _____

HOLIDAY GREETINGS		
Year	Sent	Rec

NAME _____

ADDRESS _____

CITY/STATE/ZIP _____

HOME _____OFFICE _____

E-MAIL _____FAX _____

HOLIDAY GREETINGS		
Year	Sent	Rec

NAME _____

ADDRESS _____

CITY/STATE/ZIP _____

HOME _____OFFICE _____

E-MAIL _____FAX _____

HOLIDAY GREETINGS		
Year	Sent	Rec

NAME _____

ADDRESS _____

CITY/STATE/ZIP _____

HOME _____OFFICE _____

E-MAIL _____FAX _____

HOLIDAY GREETINGS		
Year	Sent	Rec

	HOLIDAY GREETINGS		
	Year	Sent	Rec

NAME _____

ADDRESS _____

CITY/STATE/ZIP _____

HOME _____ OFFICE _____

E-MAIL _____ FAX _____

	HOLIDAY GREETINGS		
	Year	Sent	Rec

NAME _____

ADDRESS _____

CITY/STATE/ZIP _____

HOME _____ OFFICE _____

E-MAIL _____ FAX _____

	HOLIDAY GREETINGS		
	Year	Sent	Rec

NAME _____

ADDRESS _____

CITY/STATE/ZIP _____

HOME _____ OFFICE _____

E-MAIL _____ FAX _____

	HOLIDAY GREETINGS		
	Year	Sent	Rec

NAME _____

ADDRESS _____

CITY/STATE/ZIP _____

HOME _____ OFFICE _____

E-MAIL _____ FAX _____

	HOLIDAY GREETINGS		
	Year	Sent	Rec

NAME _____

ADDRESS _____

CITY/STATE/ZIP _____

HOME _____ OFFICE _____

E-MAIL _____ FAX _____

HOLIDAY GREETINGS

Year	Sent	Rec

NAME _____

ADDRESS _____

CITY/STATE/ZIP _____

HOME _____OFFICE _____

E-MAIL _____FAX _____

HOLIDAY GREETINGS

Year	Sent	Rec

NAME _____

ADDRESS _____

CITY/STATE/ZIP _____

HOME _____OFFICE _____

E-MAIL _____FAX _____

HOLIDAY GREETINGS

Year	Sent	Rec

NAME _____

ADDRESS _____

CITY/STATE/ZIP _____

HOME _____OFFICE _____

E-MAIL _____FAX _____

HOLIDAY GREETINGS

Year	Sent	Rec

NAME _____

ADDRESS _____

CITY/STATE/ZIP _____

HOME _____OFFICE _____

E-MAIL _____FAX _____

HOLIDAY GREETINGS

Year	Sent	Rec

NAME _____

ADDRESS _____

CITY/STATE/ZIP _____

HOME _____OFFICE _____

E-MAIL _____FAX _____

Summit of Mt. Humphreys
MARC MUENCH

NAME _____

ADDRESS _____

CITY/STATE/ZIP _____

HOME _____ OFFICE _____

E-MAIL _____ FAX _____

HOLIDAY GREETINGS		
Year	Sent	Rec

NAME _____

ADDRESS _____

CITY/STATE/ZIP _____

HOME _____ OFFICE _____

E-MAIL _____ FAX _____

HOLIDAY GREETINGS		
Year	Sent	Rec

NAME _____

ADDRESS _____

CITY/STATE/ZIP _____

HOME _____ OFFICE _____

E-MAIL _____ FAX _____

HOLIDAY GREETINGS		
Year	Sent	Rec

NAME _____

ADDRESS _____

CITY/STATE/ZIP _____

HOME _____ OFFICE _____

E-MAIL _____ FAX _____

HOLIDAY GREETINGS		
Year	Sent	Rec

NAME _____

ADDRESS _____

CITY/STATE/ZIP _____

HOME _____ OFFICE _____

E-MAIL _____ FAX _____

HOLIDAY GREETINGS		
Year	Sent	Rec

	HOLIDAY GREETINGS		
	Year	Sent	Rec

NAME _____

ADDRESS _____

CITY/STATE/ZIP _____

HOME _____ OFFICE _____

E-MAIL _____ FAX _____

	HOLIDAY GREETINGS		
	Year	Sent	Rec

NAME _____

ADDRESS _____

CITY/STATE/ZIP _____

HOME _____ OFFICE _____

E-MAIL _____ FAX _____

	HOLIDAY GREETINGS		
	Year	Sent	Rec

NAME _____

ADDRESS _____

CITY/STATE/ZIP _____

HOME _____ OFFICE _____

E-MAIL _____ FAX _____

	HOLIDAY GREETINGS		
	Year	Sent	Rec

NAME _____

ADDRESS _____

CITY/STATE/ZIP _____

HOME _____ OFFICE _____

E-MAIL _____ FAX _____

	HOLIDAY GREETINGS		
	Year	Sent	Rec

NAME _____

ADDRESS _____

CITY/STATE/ZIP _____

HOME _____ OFFICE _____

E-MAIL _____ FAX _____

	HOLIDAY GREETINGS		
	Year	Sent	Rec
NAME _____			
ADDRESS _____			
CITY/STATE/ZIP _____			
HOME _____ OFFICE _____			
E-MAIL _____ FAX _____			

	HOLIDAY GREETINGS		
	Year	Sent	Rec
NAME _____			
ADDRESS _____			
CITY/STATE/ZIP _____			
HOME _____ OFFICE _____			
E-MAIL _____ FAX _____			

	HOLIDAY GREETINGS		
	Year	Sent	Rec
NAME _____			
ADDRESS _____			
CITY/STATE/ZIP _____			
HOME _____ OFFICE _____			
E-MAIL _____ FAX _____			

	HOLIDAY GREETINGS		
	Year	Sent	Rec
NAME _____			
ADDRESS _____			
CITY/STATE/ZIP _____			
HOME _____ OFFICE _____			
E-MAIL _____ FAX _____			

	HOLIDAY GREETINGS		
	Year	Sent	Rec
NAME _____			
ADDRESS _____			
CITY/STATE/ZIP _____			
HOME _____ OFFICE _____			
E-MAIL _____ FAX _____			

NAME _____

ADDRESS _____

CITY/STATE/ZIP _____

HOME _____OFFICE _____

E-MAIL _____FAX _____

HOLIDAY GREETINGS		
Year	Sent	Rec

NAME _____

ADDRESS _____

CITY/STATE/ZIP _____

HOME _____OFFICE _____

E-MAIL _____FAX _____

HOLIDAY GREETINGS		
Year	Sent	Rec

NAME _____

ADDRESS _____

CITY/STATE/ZIP _____

HOME _____OFFICE _____

E-MAIL _____FAX _____

HOLIDAY GREETINGS		
Year	Sent	Rec

NAME _____

ADDRESS _____

CITY/STATE/ZIP _____

HOME _____OFFICE _____

E-MAIL _____FAX _____

HOLIDAY GREETINGS		
Year	Sent	Rec

NAME _____

ADDRESS _____

CITY/STATE/ZIP _____

HOME _____OFFICE _____

E-MAIL _____FAX _____

HOLIDAY GREETINGS		
Year	Sent	Rec

	HOLIDAY GREETINGS		
	Year	Sent	Rec

NAME _____

ADDRESS _____

CITY/STATE/ZIP _____

HOME _____ OFFICE _____

E-MAIL _____ FAX _____

	HOLIDAY GREETINGS		
	Year	Sent	Rec

NAME _____

ADDRESS _____

CITY/STATE/ZIP _____

HOME _____ OFFICE _____

E-MAIL _____ FAX _____

	HOLIDAY GREETINGS		
	Year	Sent	Rec

NAME _____

ADDRESS _____

CITY/STATE/ZIP _____

HOME _____ OFFICE _____

E-MAIL _____ FAX _____

	HOLIDAY GREETINGS		
	Year	Sent	Rec

NAME _____

ADDRESS _____

CITY/STATE/ZIP _____

HOME _____ OFFICE _____

E-MAIL _____ FAX _____

	HOLIDAY GREETINGS		
	Year	Sent	Rec

NAME _____

ADDRESS _____

CITY/STATE/ZIP _____

HOME _____ OFFICE _____

E-MAIL _____ FAX _____

NAME _____

ADDRESS _____

CITY/STATE/ZIP _____

HOME _____ OFFICE _____

E-MAIL _____ FAX _____

HOLIDAY GREETINGS		
Year	Sent	Rec

NAME _____

ADDRESS _____

CITY/STATE/ZIP _____

HOME _____ OFFICE _____

E-MAIL _____ FAX _____

HOLIDAY GREETINGS		
Year	Sent	Rec

NAME _____

ADDRESS _____

CITY/STATE/ZIP _____

HOME _____ OFFICE _____

E-MAIL _____ FAX _____

HOLIDAY GREETINGS		
Year	Sent	Rec

NAME _____

ADDRESS _____

CITY/STATE/ZIP _____

HOME _____ OFFICE _____

E-MAIL _____ FAX _____

HOLIDAY GREETINGS		
Year	Sent	Rec

NAME _____

ADDRESS _____

CITY/STATE/ZIP _____

HOME _____ OFFICE _____

E-MAIL _____ FAX _____

HOLIDAY GREETINGS		
Year	Sent	Rec

Desert storm and saguaros
JIM MARSHALL

	HOLIDAY GREETINGS		
	Year	Sent	Rec

NAME _____

ADDRESS _____

CITY/STATE/ZIP _____

HOME _____OFFICE _____

E-MAIL _____FAX _____

	HOLIDAY GREETINGS		
	Year	Sent	Rec

NAME _____

ADDRESS _____

CITY/STATE/ZIP _____

HOME _____OFFICE _____

E-MAIL _____FAX _____

	HOLIDAY GREETINGS		
	Year	Sent	Rec

NAME _____

ADDRESS _____

CITY/STATE/ZIP _____

HOME _____OFFICE _____

E-MAIL _____FAX _____

	HOLIDAY GREETINGS		
	Year	Sent	Rec

NAME _____

ADDRESS _____

CITY/STATE/ZIP _____

HOME _____OFFICE _____

E-MAIL _____FAX _____

	HOLIDAY GREETINGS		
	Year	Sent	Rec

NAME _____

ADDRESS _____

CITY/STATE/ZIP _____

HOME _____OFFICE _____

E-MAIL _____FAX _____

NAME _____

ADDRESS _____

CITY/STATE/ZIP _____

HOME _____ OFFICE _____

E-MAIL _____ FAX _____

HOLIDAY GREETINGS		
Year	Sent	Rec

NAME _____

ADDRESS _____

CITY/STATE/ZIP _____

HOME _____ OFFICE _____

E-MAIL _____ FAX _____

HOLIDAY GREETINGS		
Year	Sent	Rec

NAME _____

ADDRESS _____

CITY/STATE/ZIP _____

HOME _____ OFFICE _____

E-MAIL _____ FAX _____

HOLIDAY GREETINGS		
Year	Sent	Rec

NAME _____

ADDRESS _____

CITY/STATE/ZIP _____

HOME _____ OFFICE _____

E-MAIL _____ FAX _____

HOLIDAY GREETINGS		
Year	Sent	Rec

NAME _____

ADDRESS _____

CITY/STATE/ZIP _____

HOME _____ OFFICE _____

E-MAIL _____ FAX _____

HOLIDAY GREETINGS		
Year	Sent	Rec

NAME

NAME _____

ADDRESS _____

CITY/STATE/ZIP _____

HOME _____OFFICE _____

E-MAIL _____FAX _____

HOLIDAY GREETINGS		
Year	Sent	Rec

NAME _____

ADDRESS _____

CITY/STATE/ZIP _____

HOME _____OFFICE _____

E-MAIL _____FAX _____

HOLIDAY GREETINGS		
Year	Sent	Rec

NAME _____

ADDRESS _____

CITY/STATE/ZIP _____

HOME _____OFFICE _____

E-MAIL _____FAX _____

HOLIDAY GREETINGS		
Year	Sent	Rec

NAME _____

ADDRESS _____

CITY/STATE/ZIP _____

HOME _____OFFICE _____

E-MAIL _____FAX _____

HOLIDAY GREETINGS		
Year	Sent	Rec

NAME _____

ADDRESS _____

CITY/STATE/ZIP _____

HOME _____OFFICE _____

E-MAIL _____FAX _____

HOLIDAY GREETINGS		
Year	Sent	Rec

NAME	HOLIDAY GREETINGS		
	Year	Sent	Rec
ADDRESS			
CITY/STATE/ZIP			
HOME _____ OFFICE _____			
E-MAIL _____ FAX _____			

NAME	HOLIDAY GREETINGS		
	Year	Sent	Rec
ADDRESS			
CITY/STATE/ZIP			
HOME _____ OFFICE _____			
E-MAIL _____ FAX _____			

NAME	HOLIDAY GREETINGS		
	Year	Sent	Rec
ADDRESS			
CITY/STATE/ZIP			
HOME _____ OFFICE _____			
E-MAIL _____ FAX _____			

NAME	HOLIDAY GREETINGS		
	Year	Sent	Rec
ADDRESS			
CITY/STATE/ZIP			
HOME _____ OFFICE _____			
E-MAIL _____ FAX _____			

NAME	HOLIDAY GREETINGS		
	Year	Sent	Rec
ADDRESS			
CITY/STATE/ZIP			
HOME _____ OFFICE _____			
E-MAIL _____ FAX _____			

NAME _____

ADDRESS _____

CITY/STATE/ZIP _____

HOME _____OFFICE _____

E-MAIL _____FAX _____

HOLIDAY GREETINGS		
Year	Sent	Rec

NAME _____

ADDRESS _____

CITY/STATE/ZIP _____

HOME _____OFFICE _____

E-MAIL _____FAX _____

HOLIDAY GREETINGS		
Year	Sent	Rec

NAME _____

ADDRESS _____

CITY/STATE/ZIP _____

HOME _____OFFICE _____

E-MAIL _____FAX _____

HOLIDAY GREETINGS		
Year	Sent	Rec

NAME _____

ADDRESS _____

CITY/STATE/ZIP _____

HOME _____OFFICE _____

E-MAIL _____FAX _____

HOLIDAY GREETINGS		
Year	Sent	Rec

NAME _____

ADDRESS _____

CITY/STATE/ZIP _____

HOME _____OFFICE _____

E-MAIL _____FAX _____

HOLIDAY GREETINGS		
Year	Sent	Rec

NAME _____

ADDRESS _____

CITY/STATE/ZIP _____

HOME _____ OFFICE _____

E-MAIL _____ FAX _____

HOLIDAY GREETINGS		
Year	Sent	Rec

NAME _____

ADDRESS _____

CITY/STATE/ZIP _____

HOME _____ OFFICE _____

E-MAIL _____ FAX _____

HOLIDAY GREETINGS		
Year	Sent	Rec

NAME _____

ADDRESS _____

CITY/STATE/ZIP _____

HOME _____ OFFICE _____

E-MAIL _____ FAX _____

HOLIDAY GREETINGS		
Year	Sent	Rec

NAME _____

ADDRESS _____

CITY/STATE/ZIP _____

HOME _____ OFFICE _____

E-MAIL _____ FAX _____

HOLIDAY GREETINGS		
Year	Sent	Rec

NAME _____

ADDRESS _____

CITY/STATE/ZIP _____

HOME _____ OFFICE _____

E-MAIL _____ FAX _____

HOLIDAY GREETINGS		
Year	Sent	Rec

Yavapai Point, Grand Canyon
DICK DIETRICH

NAME _____

ADDRESS _____

CITY/STATE/ZIP _____

HOME _____ OFFICE _____

E-MAIL _____ FAX _____

HOLIDAY GREETINGS		
Year	Sent	Rec

NAME _____

ADDRESS _____

CITY/STATE/ZIP _____

HOME _____ OFFICE _____

E-MAIL _____ FAX _____

HOLIDAY GREETINGS		
Year	Sent	Rec

NAME _____

ADDRESS _____

CITY/STATE/ZIP _____

HOME _____ OFFICE _____

E-MAIL _____ FAX _____

HOLIDAY GREETINGS		
Year	Sent	Rec

NAME _____

ADDRESS _____

CITY/STATE/ZIP _____

HOME _____ OFFICE _____

E-MAIL _____ FAX _____

HOLIDAY GREETINGS		
Year	Sent	Rec

NAME _____

ADDRESS _____

CITY/STATE/ZIP _____

HOME _____ OFFICE _____

E-MAIL _____ FAX _____

HOLIDAY GREETINGS		
Year	Sent	Rec

	HOLIDAY GREETINGS		
	Year	Sent	Rec

NAME _____

ADDRESS _____

CITY/STATE/ZIP _____

HOME _____ OFFICE _____

E-MAIL _____ FAX _____

	HOLIDAY GREETINGS		
	Year	Sent	Rec

NAME _____

ADDRESS _____

CITY/STATE/ZIP _____

HOME _____ OFFICE _____

E-MAIL _____ FAX _____

	HOLIDAY GREETINGS		
	Year	Sent	Rec

NAME _____

ADDRESS _____

CITY/STATE/ZIP _____

HOME _____ OFFICE _____

E-MAIL _____ FAX _____

	HOLIDAY GREETINGS		
	Year	Sent	Rec

NAME _____

ADDRESS _____

CITY/STATE/ZIP _____

HOME _____ OFFICE _____

E-MAIL _____ FAX _____

	HOLIDAY GREETINGS		
	Year	Sent	Rec

NAME _____

ADDRESS _____

CITY/STATE/ZIP _____

HOME _____ OFFICE _____

E-MAIL _____ FAX _____

	HOLIDAY GREETINGS		
	Year	Sent	Rec

NAME _____

ADDRESS _____

CITY/STATE/ZIP _____

HOME _____ OFFICE _____

E-MAIL _____ FAX _____

	HOLIDAY GREETINGS		
	Year	Sent	Rec

NAME _____

ADDRESS _____

CITY/STATE/ZIP _____

HOME _____ OFFICE _____

E-MAIL _____ FAX _____

	HOLIDAY GREETINGS		
	Year	Sent	Rec

NAME _____

ADDRESS _____

CITY/STATE/ZIP _____

HOME _____ OFFICE _____

E-MAIL _____ FAX _____

	HOLIDAY GREETINGS		
	Year	Sent	Rec

NAME _____

ADDRESS _____

CITY/STATE/ZIP _____

HOME _____ OFFICE _____

E-MAIL _____ FAX _____

	HOLIDAY GREETINGS		
	Year	Sent	Rec

NAME _____

ADDRESS _____

CITY/STATE/ZIP _____

HOME _____ OFFICE _____

E-MAIL _____ FAX _____

NAME _____

ADDRESS _____

CITY/STATE/ZIP _____

HOME _____ OFFICE _____

E-MAIL _____ FAX _____

HOLIDAY GREETINGS		
Year	Sent	Rec

NAME _____

ADDRESS _____

CITY/STATE/ZIP _____

HOME _____ OFFICE _____

E-MAIL _____ FAX _____

HOLIDAY GREETINGS		
Year	Sent	Rec

NAME _____

ADDRESS _____

CITY/STATE/ZIP _____

HOME _____ OFFICE _____

E-MAIL _____ FAX _____

HOLIDAY GREETINGS		
Year	Sent	Rec

NAME _____

ADDRESS _____

CITY/STATE/ZIP _____

HOME _____ OFFICE _____

E-MAIL _____ FAX _____

HOLIDAY GREETINGS		
Year	Sent	Rec

NAME _____

ADDRESS _____

CITY/STATE/ZIP _____

HOME _____ OFFICE _____

E-MAIL _____ FAX _____

HOLIDAY GREETINGS		
Year	Sent	Rec

HOLIDAY GREETINGS		
Year	Sent	Rec

NAME _____

ADDRESS _____

CITY/STATE/ZIP _____

HOME _____ OFFICE _____

E-MAIL _____ FAX _____

HOLIDAY GREETINGS		
Year	Sent	Rec

NAME _____

ADDRESS _____

CITY/STATE/ZIP _____

HOME _____ OFFICE _____

E-MAIL _____ FAX _____

HOLIDAY GREETINGS		
Year	Sent	Rec

NAME _____

ADDRESS _____

CITY/STATE/ZIP _____

HOME _____ OFFICE _____

E-MAIL _____ FAX _____

HOLIDAY GREETINGS		
Year	Sent	Rec

NAME _____

ADDRESS _____

CITY/STATE/ZIP _____

HOME _____ OFFICE _____

E-MAIL _____ FAX _____

HOLIDAY GREETINGS		
Year	Sent	Rec

NAME _____

ADDRESS _____

CITY/STATE/ZIP _____

HOME _____ OFFICE _____

E-MAIL _____ FAX _____

NAME _____

ADDRESS _____

CITY/STATE/ZIP _____

HOME _____OFFICE _____

E-MAIL _____FAX _____

HOLIDAY GREETINGS		
Year	Sent	Rec

NAME _____

ADDRESS _____

CITY/STATE/ZIP _____

HOME _____OFFICE _____

E-MAIL _____FAX _____

HOLIDAY GREETINGS		
Year	Sent	Rec

NAME _____

ADDRESS _____

CITY/STATE/ZIP _____

HOME _____OFFICE _____

E-MAIL _____FAX _____

HOLIDAY GREETINGS		
Year	Sent	Rec

NAME _____

ADDRESS _____

CITY/STATE/ZIP _____

HOME _____OFFICE _____

E-MAIL _____FAX _____

HOLIDAY GREETINGS		
Year	Sent	Rec

NAME _____

ADDRESS _____

CITY/STATE/ZIP _____

HOME _____OFFICE _____

E-MAIL _____FAX _____

HOLIDAY GREETINGS		
Year	Sent	Rec

Sunset Crater

TOM DANIELSEN

NAME _____

ADDRESS _____

CITY/STATE/ZIP _____

HOME _____OFFICE _____

E-MAIL _____FAX _____

HOLIDAY GREETINGS		
Year	Sent	Rec

NAME _____

ADDRESS _____

CITY/STATE/ZIP _____

HOME _____OFFICE _____

E-MAIL _____FAX _____

HOLIDAY GREETINGS		
Year	Sent	Rec

NAME _____

ADDRESS _____

CITY/STATE/ZIP _____

HOME _____OFFICE _____

E-MAIL _____FAX _____

HOLIDAY GREETINGS		
Year	Sent	Rec

NAME _____

ADDRESS _____

CITY/STATE/ZIP _____

HOME _____OFFICE _____

E-MAIL _____FAX _____

HOLIDAY GREETINGS		
Year	Sent	Rec

NAME _____

ADDRESS _____

CITY/STATE/ZIP _____

HOME _____OFFICE _____

E-MAIL _____FAX _____

HOLIDAY GREETINGS		
Year	Sent	Rec

NAME _____

ADDRESS _____

CITY/STATE/ZIP _____

HOME _____ OFFICE _____

E-MAIL _____ FAX _____

HOLIDAY GREETINGS		
Year	Sent	Rec

NAME _____

ADDRESS _____

CITY/STATE/ZIP _____

HOME _____ OFFICE _____

E-MAIL _____ FAX _____

HOLIDAY GREETINGS		
Year	Sent	Rec

NAME _____

ADDRESS _____

CITY/STATE/ZIP _____

HOME _____ OFFICE _____

E-MAIL _____ FAX _____

HOLIDAY GREETINGS		
Year	Sent	Rec

NAME _____

ADDRESS _____

CITY/STATE/ZIP _____

HOME _____ OFFICE _____

E-MAIL _____ FAX _____

HOLIDAY GREETINGS		
Year	Sent	Rec

NAME _____

ADDRESS _____

CITY/STATE/ZIP _____

HOME _____ OFFICE _____

E-MAIL _____ FAX _____

HOLIDAY GREETINGS		
Year	Sent	Rec

	HOLIDAY GREETINGS		
	Year	Sent	Rec

NAME _____

ADDRESS _____

CITY/STATE/ZIP _____

HOME _____ OFFICE _____

E-MAIL _____ FAX _____

	HOLIDAY GREETINGS		
	Year	Sent	Rec

NAME _____

ADDRESS _____

CITY/STATE/ZIP _____

HOME _____ OFFICE _____

E-MAIL _____ FAX _____

	HOLIDAY GREETINGS		
	Year	Sent	Rec

NAME _____

ADDRESS _____

CITY/STATE/ZIP _____

HOME _____ OFFICE _____

E-MAIL _____ FAX _____

	HOLIDAY GREETINGS		
	Year	Sent	Rec

NAME _____

ADDRESS _____

CITY/STATE/ZIP _____

HOME _____ OFFICE _____

E-MAIL _____ FAX _____

	HOLIDAY GREETINGS		
	Year	Sent	Rec

NAME _____

ADDRESS _____

CITY/STATE/ZIP _____

HOME _____ OFFICE _____

E-MAIL _____ FAX _____

NAME _____

ADDRESS _____

CITY/STATE/ZIP _____

HOME _____OFFICE _____

E-MAIL _____FAX _____

HOLIDAY GREETINGS		
Year	Sent	Rec

NAME _____

ADDRESS _____

CITY/STATE/ZIP _____

HOME _____OFFICE _____

E-MAIL _____FAX _____

HOLIDAY GREETINGS		
Year	Sent	Rec

NAME _____

ADDRESS _____

CITY/STATE/ZIP _____

HOME _____OFFICE _____

E-MAIL _____FAX _____

HOLIDAY GREETINGS		
Year	Sent	Rec

NAME _____

ADDRESS _____

CITY/STATE/ZIP _____

HOME _____OFFICE _____

E-MAIL _____FAX _____

HOLIDAY GREETINGS		
Year	Sent	Rec

NAME _____

ADDRESS _____

CITY/STATE/ZIP _____

HOME _____OFFICE _____

E-MAIL _____FAX _____

HOLIDAY GREETINGS		
Year	Sent	Rec

HOLIDAY GREETINGS		
Year	Sent	Rec

NAME _____

ADDRESS _____

CITY/STATE/ZIP _____

HOME _____OFFICE _____

E-MAIL _____FAX _____

HOLIDAY GREETINGS		
Year	Sent	Rec

NAME _____

ADDRESS _____

CITY/STATE/ZIP _____

HOME _____OFFICE _____

E-MAIL _____FAX _____

HOLIDAY GREETINGS		
Year	Sent	Rec

NAME _____

ADDRESS _____

CITY/STATE/ZIP _____

HOME _____OFFICE _____

E-MAIL _____FAX _____

HOLIDAY GREETINGS		
Year	Sent	Rec

NAME _____

ADDRESS _____

CITY/STATE/ZIP _____

HOME _____OFFICE _____

E-MAIL _____FAX _____

HOLIDAY GREETINGS		
Year	Sent	Rec

NAME _____

ADDRESS _____

CITY/STATE/ZIP _____

HOME _____OFFICE _____

E-MAIL _____FAX _____

NAME _____

ADDRESS _____

CITY/STATE/ZIP _____

HOME _____ OFFICE _____

E-MAIL _____ FAX _____

HOLIDAY GREETINGS		
Year	Sent	Rec

NAME _____

ADDRESS _____

CITY/STATE/ZIP _____

HOME _____ OFFICE _____

E-MAIL _____ FAX _____

HOLIDAY GREETINGS		
Year	Sent	Rec

NAME _____

ADDRESS _____

CITY/STATE/ZIP _____

HOME _____ OFFICE _____

E-MAIL _____ FAX _____

HOLIDAY GREETINGS		
Year	Sent	Rec

NAME _____

ADDRESS _____

CITY/STATE/ZIP _____

HOME _____ OFFICE _____

E-MAIL _____ FAX _____

HOLIDAY GREETINGS		
Year	Sent	Rec

NAME _____

ADDRESS _____

CITY/STATE/ZIP _____

HOME _____ OFFICE _____

E-MAIL _____ FAX _____

HOLIDAY GREETINGS		
Year	Sent	Rec

Blue Mesa, Petrified Forest
JACK DYKINGA

NAME _____

ADDRESS _____

CITY/STATE/ZIP _____

HOME _____ OFFICE _____

E-MAIL _____ FAX _____

HOLIDAY GREETINGS		
Year	Sent	Rec

NAME _____

ADDRESS _____

CITY/STATE/ZIP _____

HOME _____ OFFICE _____

E-MAIL _____ FAX _____

HOLIDAY GREETINGS		
Year	Sent	Rec

NAME _____

ADDRESS _____

CITY/STATE/ZIP _____

HOME _____ OFFICE _____

E-MAIL _____ FAX _____

HOLIDAY GREETINGS		
Year	Sent	Rec

NAME _____

ADDRESS _____

CITY/STATE/ZIP _____

HOME _____ OFFICE _____

E-MAIL _____ FAX _____

HOLIDAY GREETINGS		
Year	Sent	Rec

NAME _____

ADDRESS _____

CITY/STATE/ZIP _____

HOME _____ OFFICE _____

E-MAIL _____ FAX _____

HOLIDAY GREETINGS		
Year	Sent	Rec

	HOLIDAY GREETINGS		
	Year	Sent	Rec

NAME _____

ADDRESS _____

CITY/STATE/ZIP _____

HOME _____ OFFICE _____

E-MAIL _____ FAX _____

	HOLIDAY GREETINGS		
	Year	Sent	Rec

NAME _____

ADDRESS _____

CITY/STATE/ZIP _____

HOME _____ OFFICE _____

E-MAIL _____ FAX _____

	HOLIDAY GREETINGS		
	Year	Sent	Rec

NAME _____

ADDRESS _____

CITY/STATE/ZIP _____

HOME _____ OFFICE _____

E-MAIL _____ FAX _____

	HOLIDAY GREETINGS		
	Year	Sent	Rec

NAME _____

ADDRESS _____

CITY/STATE/ZIP _____

HOME _____ OFFICE _____

E-MAIL _____ FAX _____

	HOLIDAY GREETINGS		
	Year	Sent	Rec

NAME _____

ADDRESS _____

CITY/STATE/ZIP _____

HOME _____ OFFICE _____

E-MAIL _____ FAX _____

NAME _____

ADDRESS _____

CITY/STATE/ZIP _____

HOME _____ OFFICE _____

E-MAIL _____ FAX _____

HOLIDAY GREETINGS		
Year	Sent	Rec

NAME _____

ADDRESS _____

CITY/STATE/ZIP _____

HOME _____ OFFICE _____

E-MAIL _____ FAX _____

HOLIDAY GREETINGS		
Year	Sent	Rec

NAME _____

ADDRESS _____

CITY/STATE/ZIP _____

HOME _____ OFFICE _____

E-MAIL _____ FAX _____

HOLIDAY GREETINGS		
Year	Sent	Rec

NAME _____

ADDRESS _____

CITY/STATE/ZIP _____

HOME _____ OFFICE _____

E-MAIL _____ FAX _____

HOLIDAY GREETINGS		
Year	Sent	Rec

NAME _____

ADDRESS _____

CITY/STATE/ZIP _____

HOME _____ OFFICE _____

E-MAIL _____ FAX _____

HOLIDAY GREETINGS		
Year	Sent	Rec

NAME _____

ADDRESS _____

CITY/STATE/ZIP _____

HOME _____OFFICE _____

E-MAIL _____FAX _____

HOLIDAY GREETINGS		
Year	Sent	Rec

NAME _____

ADDRESS _____

CITY/STATE/ZIP _____

HOME _____OFFICE _____

E-MAIL _____FAX _____

HOLIDAY GREETINGS		
Year	Sent	Rec

NAME _____

ADDRESS _____

CITY/STATE/ZIP _____

HOME _____OFFICE _____

E-MAIL _____FAX _____

HOLIDAY GREETINGS		
Year	Sent	Rec

NAME _____

ADDRESS _____

CITY/STATE/ZIP _____

HOME _____OFFICE _____

E-MAIL _____FAX _____

HOLIDAY GREETINGS		
Year	Sent	Rec

NAME _____

ADDRESS _____

CITY/STATE/ZIP _____

HOME _____OFFICE _____

E-MAIL _____FAX _____

HOLIDAY GREETINGS		
Year	Sent	Rec

	HOLIDAY GREETINGS		
	Year	Sent	Rec

NAME _____

ADDRESS _____

CITY/STATE/ZIP _____

HOME _____OFFICE _____

E-MAIL _____FAX _____

	HOLIDAY GREETINGS		
	Year	Sent	Rec

NAME _____

ADDRESS _____

CITY/STATE/ZIP _____

HOME _____OFFICE _____

E-MAIL _____FAX _____

	HOLIDAY GREETINGS		
	Year	Sent	Rec

NAME _____

ADDRESS _____

CITY/STATE/ZIP _____

HOME _____OFFICE _____

E-MAIL _____FAX _____

	HOLIDAY GREETINGS		
	Year	Sent	Rec

NAME _____

ADDRESS _____

CITY/STATE/ZIP _____

HOME _____OFFICE _____

E-MAIL _____FAX _____

	HOLIDAY GREETINGS		
	Year	Sent	Rec

NAME _____

ADDRESS _____

CITY/STATE/ZIP _____

HOME _____OFFICE _____

E-MAIL _____FAX _____

	HOLIDAY GREETINGS		
	Year	Sent	Rec

NAME _____

ADDRESS _____

CITY/STATE/ZIP _____

HOME _____ OFFICE _____

E-MAIL _____ FAX _____

	HOLIDAY GREETINGS		
	Year	Sent	Rec

NAME _____

ADDRESS _____

CITY/STATE/ZIP _____

HOME _____ OFFICE _____

E-MAIL _____ FAX _____

	HOLIDAY GREETINGS		
	Year	Sent	Rec

NAME _____

ADDRESS _____

CITY/STATE/ZIP _____

HOME _____ OFFICE _____

E-MAIL _____ FAX _____

	HOLIDAY GREETINGS		
	Year	Sent	Rec

NAME _____

ADDRESS _____

CITY/STATE/ZIP _____

HOME _____ OFFICE _____

E-MAIL _____ FAX _____

	HOLIDAY GREETINGS		
	Year	Sent	Rec

NAME _____

ADDRESS _____

CITY/STATE/ZIP _____

HOME _____ OFFICE _____

E-MAIL _____ FAX _____

Mission San Xavier del Bac

RICHARD MAACK

NAME _____

ADDRESS _____

CITY/STATE/ZIP _____

HOME _____ OFFICE _____

E-MAIL _____ FAX _____

HOLIDAY GREETINGS		
Year	Sent	Rec

NAME _____

ADDRESS _____

CITY/STATE/ZIP _____

HOME _____ OFFICE _____

E-MAIL _____ FAX _____

HOLIDAY GREETINGS		
Year	Sent	Rec

NAME _____

ADDRESS _____

CITY/STATE/ZIP _____

HOME _____ OFFICE _____

E-MAIL _____ FAX _____

HOLIDAY GREETINGS		
Year	Sent	Rec

NAME _____

ADDRESS _____

CITY/STATE/ZIP _____

HOME _____ OFFICE _____

E-MAIL _____ FAX _____

HOLIDAY GREETINGS		
Year	Sent	Rec

NAME _____

ADDRESS _____

CITY/STATE/ZIP _____

HOME _____ OFFICE _____

E-MAIL _____ FAX _____

HOLIDAY GREETINGS		
Year	Sent	Rec

NAME _____

ADDRESS _____

CITY/STATE/ZIP _____

HOME _____OFFICE _____

E-MAIL _____FAX _____

HOLIDAY GREETINGS		
Year	Sent	Rec

NAME _____

ADDRESS _____

CITY/STATE/ZIP _____

HOME _____OFFICE _____

E-MAIL _____FAX _____

HOLIDAY GREETINGS		
Year	Sent	Rec

NAME _____

ADDRESS _____

CITY/STATE/ZIP _____

HOME _____OFFICE _____

E-MAIL _____FAX _____

HOLIDAY GREETINGS		
Year	Sent	Rec

NAME _____

ADDRESS _____

CITY/STATE/ZIP _____

HOME _____OFFICE _____

E-MAIL _____FAX _____

HOLIDAY GREETINGS		
Year	Sent	Rec

NAME _____

ADDRESS _____

CITY/STATE/ZIP _____

HOME _____OFFICE _____

E-MAIL _____FAX _____

HOLIDAY GREETINGS		
Year	Sent	Rec

	HOLIDAY GREETINGS		
	Year	Sent	Rec

NAME _____

ADDRESS _____

CITY/STATE/ZIP _____

HOME _____OFFICE _____

E-MAIL _____FAX _____

	HOLIDAY GREETINGS		
	Year	Sent	Rec

NAME _____

ADDRESS _____

CITY/STATE/ZIP _____

HOME _____OFFICE _____

E-MAIL _____FAX _____

	HOLIDAY GREETINGS		
	Year	Sent	Rec

NAME _____

ADDRESS _____

CITY/STATE/ZIP _____

HOME _____OFFICE _____

E-MAIL _____FAX _____

	HOLIDAY GREETINGS		
	Year	Sent	Rec

NAME _____

ADDRESS _____

CITY/STATE/ZIP _____

HOME _____OFFICE _____

E-MAIL _____FAX _____

	HOLIDAY GREETINGS		
	Year	Sent	Rec

NAME _____

ADDRESS _____

CITY/STATE/ZIP _____

HOME _____OFFICE _____

E-MAIL _____FAX _____

HOLIDAY GREETINGS		
Year	Sent	Rec

NAME _____

ADDRESS _____

CITY/STATE/ZIP _____

HOME _____ OFFICE _____

E-MAIL _____ FAX _____

HOLIDAY GREETINGS		
Year	Sent	Rec

NAME _____

ADDRESS _____

CITY/STATE/ZIP _____

HOME _____ OFFICE _____

E-MAIL _____ FAX _____

HOLIDAY GREETINGS		
Year	Sent	Rec

NAME _____

ADDRESS _____

CITY/STATE/ZIP _____

HOME _____ OFFICE _____

E-MAIL _____ FAX _____

HOLIDAY GREETINGS		
Year	Sent	Rec

NAME _____

ADDRESS _____

CITY/STATE/ZIP _____

HOME _____ OFFICE _____

E-MAIL _____ FAX _____

HOLIDAY GREETINGS		
Year	Sent	Rec

NAME _____

ADDRESS _____

CITY/STATE/ZIP _____

HOME _____ OFFICE _____

E-MAIL _____ FAX _____

HOLIDAY GREETINGS		
Year	Sent	Rec

NAME _____

ADDRESS _____

CITY/STATE/ZIP _____

HOME _____ OFFICE _____

E-MAIL _____ FAX _____

HOLIDAY GREETINGS		
Year	Sent	Rec

NAME _____

ADDRESS _____

CITY/STATE/ZIP _____

HOME _____ OFFICE _____

E-MAIL _____ FAX _____

HOLIDAY GREETINGS		
Year	Sent	Rec

NAME _____

ADDRESS _____

CITY/STATE/ZIP _____

HOME _____ OFFICE _____

E-MAIL _____ FAX _____

HOLIDAY GREETINGS		
Year	Sent	Rec

NAME _____

ADDRESS _____

CITY/STATE/ZIP _____

HOME _____ OFFICE _____

E-MAIL _____ FAX _____

HOLIDAY GREETINGS		
Year	Sent	Rec

NAME _____

ADDRESS _____

CITY/STATE/ZIP _____

HOME _____ OFFICE _____

E-MAIL _____ FAX _____

NAME _____

ADDRESS _____

CITY/STATE/ZIP _____

HOME _____ OFFICE _____

E-MAIL _____ FAX _____

HOLIDAY GREETINGS		
Year	Sent	Rec

NAME _____

ADDRESS _____

CITY/STATE/ZIP _____

HOME _____ OFFICE _____

E-MAIL _____ FAX _____

HOLIDAY GREETINGS		
Year	Sent	Rec

NAME _____

ADDRESS _____

CITY/STATE/ZIP _____

HOME _____ OFFICE _____

E-MAIL _____ FAX _____

HOLIDAY GREETINGS		
Year	Sent	Rec

NAME _____

ADDRESS _____

CITY/STATE/ZIP _____

HOME _____ OFFICE _____

E-MAIL _____ FAX _____

HOLIDAY GREETINGS		
Year	Sent	Rec

NAME _____

ADDRESS _____

CITY/STATE/ZIP _____

HOME _____ OFFICE _____

E-MAIL _____ FAX _____

HOLIDAY GREETINGS		
Year	Sent	Rec

Santa Rita prickly pear
RANDY PRENTICE

A

B

C

D

EF

G

H

IJ

K

L

	HOLIDAY GREETINGS		
	Year	Sent	Rec

NAME _____

ADDRESS _____

CITY/STATE/ZIP _____

HOME _____ OFFICE _____

E-MAIL _____ FAX _____

	HOLIDAY GREETINGS		
	Year	Sent	Rec

NAME _____

ADDRESS _____

CITY/STATE/ZIP _____

HOME _____ OFFICE _____

E-MAIL _____ FAX _____

	HOLIDAY GREETINGS		
	Year	Sent	Rec

NAME _____

ADDRESS _____

CITY/STATE/ZIP _____

HOME _____ OFFICE _____

E-MAIL _____ FAX _____

	HOLIDAY GREETINGS		
	Year	Sent	Rec

NAME _____

ADDRESS _____

CITY/STATE/ZIP _____

HOME _____ OFFICE _____

E-MAIL _____ FAX _____

	HOLIDAY GREETINGS		
	Year	Sent	Rec

NAME _____

ADDRESS _____

CITY/STATE/ZIP _____

HOME _____ OFFICE _____

E-MAIL _____ FAX _____

	HOLIDAY GREETINGS		
	Year	Sent	Rec

NAME _____

ADDRESS _____

CITY/STATE/ZIP _____

HOME _____OFFICE _____

E-MAIL _____FAX _____

	HOLIDAY GREETINGS		
	Year	Sent	Rec

NAME _____

ADDRESS _____

CITY/STATE/ZIP _____

HOME _____OFFICE _____

E-MAIL _____FAX _____

	HOLIDAY GREETINGS		
	Year	Sent	Rec

NAME _____

ADDRESS _____

CITY/STATE/ZIP _____

HOME _____OFFICE _____

E-MAIL _____FAX _____

	HOLIDAY GREETINGS		
	Year	Sent	Rec

NAME _____

ADDRESS _____

CITY/STATE/ZIP _____

HOME _____OFFICE _____

E-MAIL _____FAX _____

	HOLIDAY GREETINGS		
	Year	Sent	Rec

NAME _____

ADDRESS _____

CITY/STATE/ZIP _____

HOME _____OFFICE _____

E-MAIL _____FAX _____

	HOLIDAY GREETINGS		
	Year	Sent	Rec

NAME _____

ADDRESS _____

CITY/STATE/ZIP _____

HOME _____OFFICE _____

E-MAIL _____FAX _____

	HOLIDAY GREETINGS		
	Year	Sent	Rec

NAME _____

ADDRESS _____

CITY/STATE/ZIP _____

HOME _____OFFICE _____

E-MAIL _____FAX _____

	HOLIDAY GREETINGS		
	Year	Sent	Rec

NAME _____

ADDRESS _____

CITY/STATE/ZIP _____

HOME _____OFFICE _____

E-MAIL _____FAX _____

	HOLIDAY GREETINGS		
	Year	Sent	Rec

NAME _____

ADDRESS _____

CITY/STATE/ZIP _____

HOME _____OFFICE _____

E-MAIL _____FAX _____

	HOLIDAY GREETINGS		
	Year	Sent	Rec

NAME _____

ADDRESS _____

CITY/STATE/ZIP _____

HOME _____OFFICE _____

E-MAIL _____FAX _____

		HOLIDAY GREETINGS		
NAME _____		Year	Sent	Rec
ADDRESS _____				
CITY/STATE/ZIP _____				
HOME _____OFFICE _____				
E-MAIL _____FAX _____				

		HOLIDAY GREETINGS		
NAME _____		Year	Sent	Rec
ADDRESS _____				
CITY/STATE/ZIP _____				
HOME _____OFFICE _____				
E-MAIL _____FAX _____				

		HOLIDAY GREETINGS		
NAME _____		Year	Sent	Rec
ADDRESS _____				
CITY/STATE/ZIP _____				
HOME _____OFFICE _____				
E-MAIL _____FAX _____				

		HOLIDAY GREETINGS		
NAME _____		Year	Sent	Rec
ADDRESS _____				
CITY/STATE/ZIP _____				
HOME _____OFFICE _____				
E-MAIL _____FAX _____				

		HOLIDAY GREETINGS		
NAME _____		Year	Sent	Rec
ADDRESS _____				
CITY/STATE/ZIP _____				
HOME _____OFFICE _____				
E-MAIL _____FAX _____				

NAME _____

ADDRESS _____

CITY/STATE/ZIP _____

HOME _____ OFFICE _____

E-MAIL _____ FAX _____

HOLIDAY GREETINGS		
Year	Sent	Rec

NAME _____

ADDRESS _____

CITY/STATE/ZIP _____

HOME _____ OFFICE _____

E-MAIL _____ FAX _____

HOLIDAY GREETINGS		
Year	Sent	Rec

NAME _____

ADDRESS _____

CITY/STATE/ZIP _____

HOME _____ OFFICE _____

E-MAIL _____ FAX _____

HOLIDAY GREETINGS		
Year	Sent	Rec

NAME _____

ADDRESS _____

CITY/STATE/ZIP _____

HOME _____ OFFICE _____

E-MAIL _____ FAX _____

HOLIDAY GREETINGS		
Year	Sent	Rec

NAME _____

ADDRESS _____

CITY/STATE/ZIP _____

HOME _____ OFFICE _____

E-MAIL _____ FAX _____

HOLIDAY GREETINGS		
Year	Sent	Rec

	HOLIDAY GREETINGS		
	Year	Sent	Rec

NAME _____

ADDRESS _____

CITY/STATE/ZIP _____

HOME _____OFFICE _____

E-MAIL _____FAX _____

	HOLIDAY GREETINGS		
	Year	Sent	Rec

NAME _____

ADDRESS _____

CITY/STATE/ZIP _____

HOME _____OFFICE _____

E-MAIL _____FAX _____

	HOLIDAY GREETINGS		
	Year	Sent	Rec

NAME _____

ADDRESS _____

CITY/STATE/ZIP _____

HOME _____OFFICE _____

E-MAIL _____FAX _____

	HOLIDAY GREETINGS		
	Year	Sent	Rec

NAME _____

ADDRESS _____

CITY/STATE/ZIP _____

HOME _____OFFICE _____

E-MAIL _____FAX _____

	HOLIDAY GREETINGS		
	Year	Sent	Rec

NAME _____

ADDRESS _____

CITY/STATE/ZIP _____

HOME _____OFFICE _____

E-MAIL _____FAX _____

Yei Bichei, Monument Valley
DICK DIETRICH

M

A

B

C

D

EF

G

H

IJ

K

L

M

HOLIDAY GREETINGS			
	Year	Sent	Rec

NAME _____

ADDRESS _____

CITY/STATE/ZIP _____

HOME _____ OFFICE _____

E-MAIL _____ FAX _____

HOLIDAY GREETINGS			
	Year	Sent	Rec

NAME _____

ADDRESS _____

CITY/STATE/ZIP _____

HOME _____ OFFICE _____

E-MAIL _____ FAX _____

HOLIDAY GREETINGS			
	Year	Sent	Rec

NAME _____

ADDRESS _____

CITY/STATE/ZIP _____

HOME _____ OFFICE _____

E-MAIL _____ FAX _____

HOLIDAY GREETINGS			
	Year	Sent	Rec

NAME _____

ADDRESS _____

CITY/STATE/ZIP _____

HOME _____ OFFICE _____

E-MAIL _____ FAX _____

HOLIDAY GREETINGS			
	Year	Sent	Rec

NAME _____

ADDRESS _____

CITY/STATE/ZIP _____

HOME _____ OFFICE _____

E-MAIL _____ FAX _____

NAME _____

ADDRESS _____

CITY/STATE/ZIP _____

HOME _____OFFICE _____

E-MAIL _____FAX _____

HOLIDAY GREETINGS		
Year	Sent	Rec

NAME _____

ADDRESS _____

CITY/STATE/ZIP _____

HOME _____OFFICE _____

E-MAIL _____FAX _____

HOLIDAY GREETINGS		
Year	Sent	Rec

NAME _____

ADDRESS _____

CITY/STATE/ZIP _____

HOME _____OFFICE _____

E-MAIL _____FAX _____

HOLIDAY GREETINGS		
Year	Sent	Rec

NAME _____

ADDRESS _____

CITY/STATE/ZIP _____

HOME _____OFFICE _____

E-MAIL _____FAX _____

HOLIDAY GREETINGS		
Year	Sent	Rec

NAME _____

ADDRESS _____

CITY/STATE/ZIP _____

HOME _____OFFICE _____

E-MAIL _____FAX _____

HOLIDAY GREETINGS		
Year	Sent	Rec

	HOLIDAY GREETINGS		
	Year	Sent	Rec

NAME _____

ADDRESS _____

CITY/STATE/ZIP _____

HOME _____ OFFICE _____

E-MAIL _____ FAX _____

	HOLIDAY GREETINGS		
	Year	Sent	Rec

NAME _____

ADDRESS _____

CITY/STATE/ZIP _____

HOME _____ OFFICE _____

E-MAIL _____ FAX _____

	HOLIDAY GREETINGS		
	Year	Sent	Rec

NAME _____

ADDRESS _____

CITY/STATE/ZIP _____

HOME _____ OFFICE _____

E-MAIL _____ FAX _____

	HOLIDAY GREETINGS		
	Year	Sent	Rec

NAME _____

ADDRESS _____

CITY/STATE/ZIP _____

HOME _____ OFFICE _____

E-MAIL _____ FAX _____

	HOLIDAY GREETINGS		
	Year	Sent	Rec

NAME _____

ADDRESS _____

CITY/STATE/ZIP _____

HOME _____ OFFICE _____

E-MAIL _____ FAX _____

	HOLIDAY GREETINGS		
	Year	Sent	Rec

NAME _____

ADDRESS _____

CITY/STATE/ZIP _____

HOME _____ OFFICE _____

E-MAIL _____ FAX _____

	HOLIDAY GREETINGS		
	Year	Sent	Rec

NAME _____

ADDRESS _____

CITY/STATE/ZIP _____

HOME _____ OFFICE _____

E-MAIL _____ FAX _____

	HOLIDAY GREETINGS		
	Year	Sent	Rec

NAME _____

ADDRESS _____

CITY/STATE/ZIP _____

HOME _____ OFFICE _____

E-MAIL _____ FAX _____

	HOLIDAY GREETINGS		
	Year	Sent	Rec

NAME _____

ADDRESS _____

CITY/STATE/ZIP _____

HOME _____ OFFICE _____

E-MAIL _____ FAX _____

	HOLIDAY GREETINGS		
	Year	Sent	Rec

NAME _____

ADDRESS _____

CITY/STATE/ZIP _____

HOME _____ OFFICE _____

E-MAIL _____ FAX _____

	HOLIDAY GREETINGS		
	Year	Sent	Rec.

NAME _____

ADDRESS _____

CITY/STATE/ZIP _____

HOME _____ OFFICE _____

E-MAIL _____ FAX _____

	HOLIDAY GREETINGS		
	Year	Sent	Rec.

NAME _____

ADDRESS _____

CITY/STATE/ZIP _____

HOME _____ OFFICE _____

E-MAIL _____ FAX _____

	HOLIDAY GREETINGS		
	Year	Sent	Rec.

NAME _____

ADDRESS _____

CITY/STATE/ZIP _____

HOME _____ OFFICE _____

E-MAIL _____ FAX _____

	HOLIDAY GREETINGS		
	Year	Sent	Rec.

NAME _____

ADDRESS _____

CITY/STATE/ZIP _____

HOME _____ OFFICE _____

E-MAIL _____ FAX _____

	HOLIDAY GREETINGS		
	Year	Sent	Rec.

NAME _____

ADDRESS _____

CITY/STATE/ZIP _____

HOME _____ OFFICE _____

E-MAIL _____ FAX _____

	HOLIDAY GREETINGS		
	Year	Sent	Rec

NAME _____

ADDRESS _____

CITY/STATE/ZIP _____

HOME _____OFFICE _____

E-MAIL _____FAX _____

	HOLIDAY GREETINGS		
	Year	Sent	Rec

NAME _____

ADDRESS _____

CITY/STATE/ZIP _____

HOME _____OFFICE _____

E-MAIL _____FAX _____

	HOLIDAY GREETINGS		
	Year	Sent	Rec

NAME _____

ADDRESS _____

CITY/STATE/ZIP _____

HOME _____OFFICE _____

E-MAIL _____FAX _____

	HOLIDAY GREETINGS		
	Year	Sent	Rec

NAME _____

ADDRESS _____

CITY/STATE/ZIP _____

HOME _____OFFICE _____

E-MAIL _____FAX _____

	HOLIDAY GREETINGS		
	Year	Sent	Rec

NAME _____

ADDRESS _____

CITY/STATE/ZIP _____

HOME _____OFFICE _____

E-MAIL _____FAX _____

Oak Creek Canyon
BOB & SUZANNE CLEMENZ

NAME _____

ADDRESS _____

CITY/STATE/ZIP _____

HOME _____OFFICE _____

E-MAIL _____FAX _____

HOLIDAY GREETINGS		
Year	Sent	Rec

NAME _____

ADDRESS _____

CITY/STATE/ZIP _____

HOME _____OFFICE _____

E-MAIL _____FAX _____

HOLIDAY GREETINGS		
Year	Sent	Rec

NAME _____

ADDRESS _____

CITY/STATE/ZIP _____

HOME _____OFFICE _____

E-MAIL _____FAX _____

HOLIDAY GREETINGS		
Year	Sent	Rec

NAME _____

ADDRESS _____

CITY/STATE/ZIP _____

HOME _____OFFICE _____

E-MAIL _____FAX _____

HOLIDAY GREETINGS		
Year	Sent	Rec

NAME _____

ADDRESS _____

CITY/STATE/ZIP _____

HOME _____OFFICE _____

E-MAIL _____FAX _____

HOLIDAY GREETINGS		
Year	Sent	Rec

NAME _____

ADDRESS _____

CITY/STATE/ZIP _____

HOME _____ OFFICE _____

E-MAIL _____ FAX _____

HOLIDAY GREETINGS		
Year	Sent	Rec

NAME _____

ADDRESS _____

CITY/STATE/ZIP _____

HOME _____ OFFICE _____

E-MAIL _____ FAX _____

HOLIDAY GREETINGS		
Year	Sent	Rec

NAME _____

ADDRESS _____

CITY/STATE/ZIP _____

HOME _____ OFFICE _____

E-MAIL _____ FAX _____

HOLIDAY GREETINGS		
Year	Sent	Rec

NAME _____

ADDRESS _____

CITY/STATE/ZIP _____

HOME _____ OFFICE _____

E-MAIL _____ FAX _____

HOLIDAY GREETINGS		
Year	Sent	Rec

NAME _____

ADDRESS _____

CITY/STATE/ZIP _____

HOME _____ OFFICE _____

E-MAIL _____ FAX _____

HOLIDAY GREETINGS		
Year	Sent	Rec

NAME _____	HOLIDAY GREETINGS		
	Year	Sent	Rec
ADDRESS _____			
CITY/STATE/ZIP _____			
HOME _____ OFFICE _____			
E-MAIL _____ FAX _____			

NAME _____	HOLIDAY GREETINGS		
	Year	Sent	Rec
ADDRESS _____			
CITY/STATE/ZIP _____			
HOME _____ OFFICE _____			
E-MAIL _____ FAX _____			

NAME _____	HOLIDAY GREETINGS		
	Year	Sent	Rec
ADDRESS _____			
CITY/STATE/ZIP _____			
HOME _____ OFFICE _____			
E-MAIL _____ FAX _____			

NAME _____	HOLIDAY GREETINGS		
	Year	Sent	Rec
ADDRESS _____			
CITY/STATE/ZIP _____			
HOME _____ OFFICE _____			
E-MAIL _____ FAX _____			

NAME _____	HOLIDAY GREETINGS		
	Year	Sent	Rec
ADDRESS _____			
CITY/STATE/ZIP _____			
HOME _____ OFFICE _____			
E-MAIL _____ FAX _____			

	HOLIDAY GREETINGS		
	Year	Sent	Rec

NAME _____

ADDRESS _____

CITY/STATE/ZIP _____

HOME _____OFFICE _____

E-MAIL _____FAX _____

	HOLIDAY GREETINGS		
	Year	Sent	Rec

NAME _____

ADDRESS _____

CITY/STATE/ZIP _____

HOME _____OFFICE _____

E-MAIL _____FAX _____

	HOLIDAY GREETINGS		
	Year	Sent	Rec

NAME _____

ADDRESS _____

CITY/STATE/ZIP _____

HOME _____OFFICE _____

E-MAIL _____FAX _____

	HOLIDAY GREETINGS		
	Year	Sent	Rec

NAME _____

ADDRESS _____

CITY/STATE/ZIP _____

HOME _____OFFICE _____

E-MAIL _____FAX _____

	HOLIDAY GREETINGS		
	Year	Sent	Rec

NAME _____

ADDRESS _____

CITY/STATE/ZIP _____

HOME _____OFFICE _____

E-MAIL _____FAX _____

HOLIDAY GREETINGS		
Year	Sent	Rec

NAME _____

ADDRESS _____

CITY/STATE/ZIP _____

HOME _____ OFFICE _____

E-MAIL _____ FAX _____

HOLIDAY GREETINGS		
Year	Sent	Rec

NAME _____

ADDRESS _____

CITY/STATE/ZIP _____

HOME _____ OFFICE _____

E-MAIL _____ FAX _____

HOLIDAY GREETINGS		
Year	Sent	Rec

NAME _____

ADDRESS _____

CITY/STATE/ZIP _____

HOME _____ OFFICE _____

E-MAIL _____ FAX _____

HOLIDAY GREETINGS		
Year	Sent	Rec

NAME _____

ADDRESS _____

CITY/STATE/ZIP _____

HOME _____ OFFICE _____

E-MAIL _____ FAX _____

HOLIDAY GREETINGS		
Year	Sent	Rec

NAME _____

ADDRESS _____

CITY/STATE/ZIP _____

HOME _____ OFFICE _____

E-MAIL _____ FAX _____

NAME _____

ADDRESS _____

CITY/STATE/ZIP _____

HOME _____ OFFICE _____

E-MAIL _____ FAX _____

HOLIDAY GREETINGS		
Year	Sent	Rec

NAME _____

ADDRESS _____

CITY/STATE/ZIP _____

HOME _____ OFFICE _____

E-MAIL _____ FAX _____

HOLIDAY GREETINGS		
Year	Sent	Rec

NAME _____

ADDRESS _____

CITY/STATE/ZIP _____

HOME _____ OFFICE _____

E-MAIL _____ FAX _____

HOLIDAY GREETINGS		
Year	Sent	Rec

NAME _____

ADDRESS _____

CITY/STATE/ZIP _____

HOME _____ OFFICE _____

E-MAIL _____ FAX _____

HOLIDAY GREETINGS		
Year	Sent	Rec

NAME _____

ADDRESS _____

CITY/STATE/ZIP _____

HOME _____ OFFICE _____

E-MAIL _____ FAX _____

HOLIDAY GREETINGS		
Year	Sent	Rec

O

Grand Falls
RICHARD STRANGE

A

B

C

D

EF

G

H

IJ

K

L

M

N

O

HOLIDAY GREETINGS		
Year	Sent	Rec

NAME _____

ADDRESS _____

CITY/STATE/ZIP _____

HOME _____ OFFICE _____

E-MAIL _____ FAX _____

HOLIDAY GREETINGS		
Year	Sent	Rec

NAME _____

ADDRESS _____

CITY/STATE/ZIP _____

HOME _____ OFFICE _____

E-MAIL _____ FAX _____

HOLIDAY GREETINGS		
Year	Sent	Rec

NAME _____

ADDRESS _____

CITY/STATE/ZIP _____

HOME _____ OFFICE _____

E-MAIL _____ FAX _____

HOLIDAY GREETINGS		
Year	Sent	Rec

NAME _____

ADDRESS _____

CITY/STATE/ZIP _____

HOME _____ OFFICE _____

E-MAIL _____ FAX _____

HOLIDAY GREETINGS		
Year	Sent	Rec

NAME _____

ADDRESS _____

CITY/STATE/ZIP _____

HOME _____ OFFICE _____

E-MAIL _____ FAX _____

NAME _____

HOLIDAY GREETINGS		
Year	Sent	Rec

ADDRESS _____

CITY/STATE/ZIP _____

HOME _____OFFICE _____

E-MAIL _____FAX _____

NAME _____

HOLIDAY GREETINGS		
Year	Sent	Rec

ADDRESS _____

CITY/STATE/ZIP _____

HOME _____OFFICE _____

E-MAIL _____FAX _____

NAME _____

HOLIDAY GREETINGS		
Year	Sent	Rec

ADDRESS _____

CITY/STATE/ZIP _____

HOME _____OFFICE _____

E-MAIL _____FAX _____

NAME _____

HOLIDAY GREETINGS		
Year	Sent	Rec

ADDRESS _____

CITY/STATE/ZIP _____

HOME _____OFFICE _____

E-MAIL _____FAX _____

NAME _____

HOLIDAY GREETINGS		
Year	Sent	Rec

ADDRESS _____

CITY/STATE/ZIP _____

HOME _____OFFICE _____

E-MAIL _____FAX _____

	HOLIDAY GREETINGS		
	Year	Sent	Rec

NAME _____

ADDRESS _____

CITY/STATE/ZIP _____

HOME _____ OFFICE _____

E-MAIL _____ FAX _____

	HOLIDAY GREETINGS		
	Year	Sent	Rec

NAME _____

ADDRESS _____

CITY/STATE/ZIP _____

HOME _____ OFFICE _____

E-MAIL _____ FAX _____

	HOLIDAY GREETINGS		
	Year	Sent	Rec

NAME _____

ADDRESS _____

CITY/STATE/ZIP _____

HOME _____ OFFICE _____

E-MAIL _____ FAX _____

	HOLIDAY GREETINGS		
	Year	Sent	Rec

NAME _____

ADDRESS _____

CITY/STATE/ZIP _____

HOME _____ OFFICE _____

E-MAIL _____ FAX _____

	HOLIDAY GREETINGS		
	Year	Sent	Rec

NAME _____

ADDRESS _____

CITY/STATE/ZIP _____

HOME _____ OFFICE _____

E-MAIL _____ FAX _____

NAME _____	HOLIDAY GREETINGS		
	Year	Sent	Rec
ADDRESS _____			
CITY/STATE/ZIP _____			
HOME _____ OFFICE _____			
E-MAIL _____ FAX _____			

NAME _____	HOLIDAY GREETINGS		
	Year	Sent	Rec
ADDRESS _____			
CITY/STATE/ZIP _____			
HOME _____ OFFICE _____			
E-MAIL _____ FAX _____			

NAME _____	HOLIDAY GREETINGS		
	Year	Sent	Rec
ADDRESS _____			
CITY/STATE/ZIP _____			
HOME _____ OFFICE _____			
E-MAIL _____ FAX _____			

NAME _____	HOLIDAY GREETINGS		
	Year	Sent	Rec
ADDRESS _____			
CITY/STATE/ZIP _____			
HOME _____ OFFICE _____			
E-MAIL _____ FAX _____			

NAME _____	HOLIDAY GREETINGS		
	Year	Sent	Rec
ADDRESS _____			
CITY/STATE/ZIP _____			
HOME _____ OFFICE _____			
E-MAIL _____ FAX _____			

	HOLIDAY GREETINGS		
	Year	Sent	Rec

NAME _____

ADDRESS _____

CITY/STATE/ZIP _____

HOME _____OFFICE _____

E-MAIL _____FAX _____

	HOLIDAY GREETINGS		
	Year	Sent	Rec

NAME _____

ADDRESS _____

CITY/STATE/ZIP _____

HOME _____OFFICE _____

E-MAIL _____FAX _____

	HOLIDAY GREETINGS		
	Year	Sent	Rec

NAME _____

ADDRESS _____

CITY/STATE/ZIP _____

HOME _____OFFICE _____

E-MAIL _____FAX _____

	HOLIDAY GREETINGS		
	Year	Sent	Rec

NAME _____

ADDRESS _____

CITY/STATE/ZIP _____

HOME _____OFFICE _____

E-MAIL _____FAX _____

	HOLIDAY GREETINGS		
	Year	Sent	Rec

NAME _____

ADDRESS _____

CITY/STATE/ZIP _____

HOME _____OFFICE _____

E-MAIL _____FAX _____

NAME _____		HOLIDAY GREETINGS		
		Year	Sent	Rec
ADDRESS _____				
CITY/STATE/ZIP _____				
HOME _____OFFICE _____				
E-MAIL _____FAX _____				

NAME _____		HOLIDAY GREETINGS		
		Year	Sent	Rec
ADDRESS _____				
CITY/STATE/ZIP _____				
HOME _____OFFICE _____				
E-MAIL _____FAX _____				

NAME _____		HOLIDAY GREETINGS		
		Year	Sent	Rec
ADDRESS _____				
CITY/STATE/ZIP _____				
HOME _____OFFICE _____				
E-MAIL _____FAX _____				

NAME _____		HOLIDAY GREETINGS		
		Year	Sent	Rec
ADDRESS _____				
CITY/STATE/ZIP _____				
HOME _____OFFICE _____				
E-MAIL _____FAX _____				

NAME _____		HOLIDAY GREETINGS		
		Year	Sent	Rec
ADDRESS _____				
CITY/STATE/ZIP _____				
HOME _____OFFICE _____				
E-MAIL _____FAX _____				

Montezuma Castle
GEORGE H.H. HUEY

A

B

C

D

EF

G

H

IJ

K

L

M

N

O

PQ

HOLIDAY GREETINGS		
Year	Sent	Rec

NAME _____

ADDRESS _____

CITY/STATE/ZIP _____

HOME _____ OFFICE _____

E-MAIL _____ FAX _____

HOLIDAY GREETINGS		
Year	Sent	Rec

NAME _____

ADDRESS _____

CITY/STATE/ZIP _____

HOME _____ OFFICE _____

E-MAIL _____ FAX _____

HOLIDAY GREETINGS		
Year	Sent	Rec

NAME _____

ADDRESS _____

CITY/STATE/ZIP _____

HOME _____ OFFICE _____

E-MAIL _____ FAX _____

HOLIDAY GREETINGS		
Year	Sent	Rec

NAME _____

ADDRESS _____

CITY/STATE/ZIP _____

HOME _____ OFFICE _____

E-MAIL _____ FAX _____

HOLIDAY GREETINGS		
Year	Sent	Rec

NAME _____

ADDRESS _____

CITY/STATE/ZIP _____

HOME _____ OFFICE _____

E-MAIL _____ FAX _____

HOLIDAY GREETINGS		
Year	Sent	Rec

NAME _____

ADDRESS _____

CITY/STATE/ZIP _____

HOME _____OFFICE _____

E-MAIL _____FAX _____

HOLIDAY GREETINGS		
Year	Sent	Rec

NAME _____

ADDRESS _____

CITY/STATE/ZIP _____

HOME _____OFFICE _____

E-MAIL _____FAX _____

HOLIDAY GREETINGS		
Year	Sent	Rec

NAME _____

ADDRESS _____

CITY/STATE/ZIP _____

HOME _____OFFICE _____

E-MAIL _____FAX _____

HOLIDAY GREETINGS		
Year	Sent	Rec

NAME _____

ADDRESS _____

CITY/STATE/ZIP _____

HOME _____OFFICE _____

E-MAIL _____FAX _____

HOLIDAY GREETINGS		
Year	Sent	Rec

NAME _____

ADDRESS _____

CITY/STATE/ZIP _____

HOME _____OFFICE _____

E-MAIL _____FAX _____

	HOLIDAY GREETINGS		
	Year	Sent	Rec

NAME _____

ADDRESS _____

CITY/STATE/ZIP _____

HOME _____OFFICE _____

E-MAIL _____FAX _____

	HOLIDAY GREETINGS		
	Year	Sent	Rec

NAME _____

ADDRESS _____

CITY/STATE/ZIP _____

HOME _____OFFICE _____

E-MAIL _____FAX _____

	HOLIDAY GREETINGS		
	Year	Sent	Rec

NAME _____

ADDRESS _____

CITY/STATE/ZIP _____

HOME _____OFFICE _____

E-MAIL _____FAX _____

	HOLIDAY GREETINGS		
	Year	Sent	Rec

NAME _____

ADDRESS _____

CITY/STATE/ZIP _____

HOME _____OFFICE _____

E-MAIL _____FAX _____

	HOLIDAY GREETINGS		
	Year	Sent	Rec

NAME _____

ADDRESS _____

CITY/STATE/ZIP _____

HOME _____OFFICE _____

E-MAIL _____FAX _____

NAME _____	HOLIDAY GREETINGS		
	Year	Sent	Rec
ADDRESS _____			
CITY/STATE/ZIP _____			
HOME _____OFFICE _____			
E-MAIL _____FAX _____			

NAME _____	HOLIDAY GREETINGS		
	Year	Sent	Rec
ADDRESS _____			
CITY/STATE/ZIP _____			
HOME _____OFFICE _____			
E-MAIL _____FAX _____			

NAME _____	HOLIDAY GREETINGS		
	Year	Sent	Rec
ADDRESS _____			
CITY/STATE/ZIP _____			
HOME _____OFFICE _____			
E-MAIL _____FAX _____			

NAME _____	HOLIDAY GREETINGS		
	Year	Sent	Rec
ADDRESS _____			
CITY/STATE/ZIP _____			
HOME _____OFFICE _____			
E-MAIL _____FAX _____			

NAME _____	HOLIDAY GREETINGS		
	Year	Sent	Rec
ADDRESS _____			
CITY/STATE/ZIP _____			
HOME _____OFFICE _____			
E-MAIL _____FAX _____			

NAME _____

ADDRESS _____

CITY/STATE/ZIP _____

HOME _____OFFICE _____

E-MAIL _____FAX _____

HOLIDAY GREETINGS		
Year	Sent	Rec

NAME _____

ADDRESS _____

CITY/STATE/ZIP _____

HOME _____OFFICE _____

E-MAIL _____FAX _____

HOLIDAY GREETINGS		
Year	Sent	Rec

NAME _____

ADDRESS _____

CITY/STATE/ZIP _____

HOME _____OFFICE _____

E-MAIL _____FAX _____

HOLIDAY GREETINGS		
Year	Sent	Rec

NAME _____

ADDRESS _____

CITY/STATE/ZIP _____

HOME _____OFFICE _____

E-MAIL _____FAX _____

HOLIDAY GREETINGS		
Year	Sent	Rec

NAME _____

ADDRESS _____

CITY/STATE/ZIP _____

HOME _____OFFICE _____

E-MAIL _____FAX _____

HOLIDAY GREETINGS		
Year	Sent	Rec

	HOLIDAY GREETINGS		
	Year	Sent	Rec

NAME _____

ADDRESS _____

CITY/STATE/ZIP _____

HOME _____OFFICE _____

E-MAIL _____FAX _____

	HOLIDAY GREETINGS		
	Year	Sent	Rec

NAME _____

ADDRESS _____

CITY/STATE/ZIP _____

HOME _____OFFICE _____

E-MAIL _____FAX _____

	HOLIDAY GREETINGS		
	Year	Sent	Rec

NAME _____

ADDRESS _____

CITY/STATE/ZIP _____

HOME _____OFFICE _____

E-MAIL _____FAX _____

	HOLIDAY GREETINGS		
	Year	Sent	Rec

NAME _____

ADDRESS _____

CITY/STATE/ZIP _____

HOME _____OFFICE _____

E-MAIL _____FAX _____

	HOLIDAY GREETINGS		
	Year	Sent	Rec

NAME _____

ADDRESS _____

CITY/STATE/ZIP _____

HOME _____OFFICE _____

E-MAIL _____FAX _____

Sheepherding in Monument Valley
ARTHUR MULLIN

A

B

C

D

EF

G

H

IJ

K

L

M

N

O

PQ

R

HOLIDAY GREETINGS		
Year	Sent	Rec

NAME _____

ADDRESS _____

CITY/STATE/ZIP _____

HOME _____OFFICE _____

E-MAIL _____FAX _____

HOLIDAY GREETINGS		
Year	Sent	Rec

NAME _____

ADDRESS _____

CITY/STATE/ZIP _____

HOME _____OFFICE _____

E-MAIL _____FAX _____

HOLIDAY GREETINGS		
Year	Sent	Rec

NAME _____

ADDRESS _____

CITY/STATE/ZIP _____

HOME _____OFFICE _____

E-MAIL _____FAX _____

HOLIDAY GREETINGS		
Year	Sent	Rec

NAME _____

ADDRESS _____

CITY/STATE/ZIP _____

HOME _____OFFICE _____

E-MAIL _____FAX _____

HOLIDAY GREETINGS		
Year	Sent	Rec

NAME _____

ADDRESS _____

CITY/STATE/ZIP _____

HOME _____OFFICE _____

E-MAIL _____FAX _____

NAME _____

ADDRESS _____

CITY/STATE/ZIP _____

HOME _____OFFICE _____

E-MAIL _____FAX _____

HOLIDAY GREETINGS		
Year	Sent	Rec

NAME _____

ADDRESS _____

CITY/STATE/ZIP _____

HOME _____OFFICE _____

E-MAIL _____FAX _____

HOLIDAY GREETINGS		
Year	Sent	Rec

NAME _____

ADDRESS _____

CITY/STATE/ZIP _____

HOME _____OFFICE _____

E-MAIL _____FAX _____

HOLIDAY GREETINGS		
Year	Sent	Rec

NAME _____

ADDRESS _____

CITY/STATE/ZIP _____

HOME _____OFFICE _____

E-MAIL _____FAX _____

HOLIDAY GREETINGS		
Year	Sent	Rec

NAME _____

ADDRESS _____

CITY/STATE/ZIP _____

HOME _____OFFICE _____

E-MAIL _____FAX _____

HOLIDAY GREETINGS		
Year	Sent	Rec

NAME _____	HOLIDAY GREETINGS		
	Year	Sent	Rec
ADDRESS _____			
CITY/STATE/ZIP _____			
HOME _____ OFFICE _____			
E-MAIL _____ FAX _____			

NAME _____	HOLIDAY GREETINGS		
	Year	Sent	Rec
ADDRESS _____			
CITY/STATE/ZIP _____			
HOME _____ OFFICE _____			
E-MAIL _____ FAX _____			

NAME _____	HOLIDAY GREETINGS		
	Year	Sent	Rec
ADDRESS _____			
CITY/STATE/ZIP _____			
HOME _____ OFFICE _____			
E-MAIL _____ FAX _____			

NAME _____	HOLIDAY GREETINGS		
	Year	Sent	Rec
ADDRESS _____			
CITY/STATE/ZIP _____			
HOME _____ OFFICE _____			
E-MAIL _____ FAX _____			

NAME _____	HOLIDAY GREETINGS		
	Year	Sent	Rec
ADDRESS _____			
CITY/STATE/ZIP _____			
HOME _____ OFFICE _____			
E-MAIL _____ FAX _____			

HOLIDAY GREETINGS		
Year	Sent	Rec

NAME _____

ADDRESS _____

CITY/STATE/ZIP _____

HOME _____ OFFICE _____

E-MAIL _____ FAX _____

HOLIDAY GREETINGS		
Year	Sent	Rec

NAME _____

ADDRESS _____

CITY/STATE/ZIP _____

HOME _____ OFFICE _____

E-MAIL _____ FAX _____

HOLIDAY GREETINGS		
Year	Sent	Rec

NAME _____

ADDRESS _____

CITY/STATE/ZIP _____

HOME _____ OFFICE _____

E-MAIL _____ FAX _____

HOLIDAY GREETINGS		
Year	Sent	Rec

NAME _____

ADDRESS _____

CITY/STATE/ZIP _____

HOME _____ OFFICE _____

E-MAIL _____ FAX _____

HOLIDAY GREETINGS		
Year	Sent	Rec

NAME _____

ADDRESS _____

CITY/STATE/ZIP _____

HOME _____ OFFICE _____

E-MAIL _____ FAX _____

	HOLIDAY GREETINGS		
	Year	Sent	Rec

NAME _____

ADDRESS _____

CITY/STATE/ZIP _____

HOME _____OFFICE _____

E-MAIL _____FAX _____

	HOLIDAY GREETINGS		
	Year	Sent	Rec

NAME _____

ADDRESS _____

CITY/STATE/ZIP _____

HOME _____OFFICE _____

E-MAIL _____FAX _____

	HOLIDAY GREETINGS		
	Year	Sent	Rec

NAME _____

ADDRESS _____

CITY/STATE/ZIP _____

HOME _____OFFICE _____

E-MAIL _____FAX _____

	HOLIDAY GREETINGS		
	Year	Sent	Rec

NAME _____

ADDRESS _____

CITY/STATE/ZIP _____

HOME _____OFFICE _____

E-MAIL _____FAX _____

	HOLIDAY GREETINGS		
	Year	Sent	Rec

NAME _____

ADDRESS _____

CITY/STATE/ZIP _____

HOME _____OFFICE _____

E-MAIL _____FAX _____

NAME _____

ADDRESS _____

CITY/STATE/ZIP _____

HOME _____ OFFICE _____

E-MAIL _____ FAX _____

HOLIDAY GREETINGS		
Year	Sent	Rec

NAME _____

ADDRESS _____

CITY/STATE/ZIP _____

HOME _____ OFFICE _____

E-MAIL _____ FAX _____

HOLIDAY GREETINGS		
Year	Sent	Rec

NAME _____

ADDRESS _____

CITY/STATE/ZIP _____

HOME _____ OFFICE _____

E-MAIL _____ FAX _____

HOLIDAY GREETINGS		
Year	Sent	Rec

NAME _____

ADDRESS _____

CITY/STATE/ZIP _____

HOME _____ OFFICE _____

E-MAIL _____ FAX _____

HOLIDAY GREETINGS		
Year	Sent	Rec

NAME _____

ADDRESS _____

CITY/STATE/ZIP _____

HOME _____ OFFICE _____

E-MAIL _____ FAX _____

HOLIDAY GREETINGS		
Year	Sent	Rec

Fresh snow in Oak Creek
RALPH HOPKINS

A

B

C

D

EF

G

H

IJ

K

L

M

N

O

PQ

R

S

NAME _____		
ADDRESS _____		
CITY/STATE/ZIP _____		
HOME _____ OFFICE _____		
E-MAIL _____ FAX _____		

HOLIDAY GREETINGS

Year	Sent	Rec

NAME _____		
ADDRESS _____		
CITY/STATE/ZIP _____		
HOME _____ OFFICE _____		
E-MAIL _____ FAX _____		

HOLIDAY GREETINGS

Year	Sent	Rec

NAME _____		
ADDRESS _____		
CITY/STATE/ZIP _____		
HOME _____ OFFICE _____		
E-MAIL _____ FAX _____		

HOLIDAY GREETINGS

Year	Sent	Rec

NAME _____		
ADDRESS _____		
CITY/STATE/ZIP _____		
HOME _____ OFFICE _____		
E-MAIL _____ FAX _____		

HOLIDAY GREETINGS

Year	Sent	Rec

NAME _____		
ADDRESS _____		
CITY/STATE/ZIP _____		
HOME _____ OFFICE _____		
E-MAIL _____ FAX _____		

HOLIDAY GREETINGS

Year	Sent	Rec

NAME _____

ADDRESS _____

CITY/STATE/ZIP _____

HOME _____ OFFICE _____

E-MAIL _____ FAX _____

HOLIDAY GREETINGS		
Year	Sent	Rec

NAME _____

ADDRESS _____

CITY/STATE/ZIP _____

HOME _____ OFFICE _____

E-MAIL _____ FAX _____

HOLIDAY GREETINGS		
Year	Sent	Rec

NAME _____

ADDRESS _____

CITY/STATE/ZIP _____

HOME _____ OFFICE _____

E-MAIL _____ FAX _____

HOLIDAY GREETINGS		
Year	Sent	Rec

NAME _____

ADDRESS _____

CITY/STATE/ZIP _____

HOME _____ OFFICE _____

E-MAIL _____ FAX _____

HOLIDAY GREETINGS		
Year	Sent	Rec

NAME _____

ADDRESS _____

CITY/STATE/ZIP _____

HOME _____ OFFICE _____

E-MAIL _____ FAX _____

HOLIDAY GREETINGS		
Year	Sent	Rec

NAME _____

ADDRESS _____

CITY/STATE/ZIP _____

HOME _____ OFFICE _____

E-MAIL _____ FAX _____

HOLIDAY GREETINGS		
Year	Sent	Rec

NAME _____

ADDRESS _____

CITY/STATE/ZIP _____

HOME _____ OFFICE _____

E-MAIL _____ FAX _____

HOLIDAY GREETINGS		
Year	Sent	Rec

NAME _____

ADDRESS _____

CITY/STATE/ZIP _____

HOME _____ OFFICE _____

E-MAIL _____ FAX _____

HOLIDAY GREETINGS		
Year	Sent	Rec

NAME _____

ADDRESS _____

CITY/STATE/ZIP _____

HOME _____ OFFICE _____

E-MAIL _____ FAX _____

HOLIDAY GREETINGS		
Year	Sent	Rec

NAME _____

ADDRESS _____

CITY/STATE/ZIP _____

HOME _____ OFFICE _____

E-MAIL _____ FAX _____

HOLIDAY GREETINGS		
Year	Sent	Rec

NAME _____

ADDRESS _____

CITY/STATE/ZIP _____

HOME _____ OFFICE _____

E-MAIL _____ FAX _____

HOLIDAY GREETINGS		
Year	Sent	Rec

NAME _____

ADDRESS _____

CITY/STATE/ZIP _____

HOME _____ OFFICE _____

E-MAIL _____ FAX _____

HOLIDAY GREETINGS		
Year	Sent	Rec

NAME _____

ADDRESS _____

CITY/STATE/ZIP _____

HOME _____ OFFICE _____

E-MAIL _____ FAX _____

HOLIDAY GREETINGS		
Year	Sent	Rec

NAME _____

ADDRESS _____

CITY/STATE/ZIP _____

HOME _____ OFFICE _____

E-MAIL _____ FAX _____

HOLIDAY GREETINGS		
Year	Sent	Rec

NAME _____

ADDRESS _____

CITY/STATE/ZIP _____

HOME _____ OFFICE _____

E-MAIL _____ FAX _____

HOLIDAY GREETINGS		
Year	Sent	Rec

	HOLIDAY GREETINGS		
	Year	Sent	Rec

NAME _____

ADDRESS _____

CITY/STATE/ZIP _____

HOME _____OFFICE _____

E-MAIL _____FAX _____

	HOLIDAY GREETINGS		
	Year	Sent	Rec

NAME _____

ADDRESS _____

CITY/STATE/ZIP _____

HOME _____OFFICE _____

E-MAIL _____FAX _____

	HOLIDAY GREETINGS		
	Year	Sent	Rec

NAME _____

ADDRESS _____

CITY/STATE/ZIP _____

HOME _____OFFICE _____

E-MAIL _____FAX _____

	HOLIDAY GREETINGS		
	Year	Sent	Rec

NAME _____

ADDRESS _____

CITY/STATE/ZIP _____

HOME _____OFFICE _____

E-MAIL _____FAX _____

	HOLIDAY GREETINGS		
	Year	Sent	Rec

NAME _____

ADDRESS _____

CITY/STATE/ZIP _____

HOME _____OFFICE _____

E-MAIL _____FAX _____

NAME _____

ADDRESS _____

CITY/STATE/ZIP _____

HOME _____ OFFICE _____

E-MAIL _____ FAX _____

HOLIDAY GREETINGS		
Year	Sent	Rec

NAME _____

ADDRESS _____

CITY/STATE/ZIP _____

HOME _____ OFFICE _____

E-MAIL _____ FAX _____

HOLIDAY GREETINGS		
Year	Sent	Rec

NAME _____

ADDRESS _____

CITY/STATE/ZIP _____

HOME _____ OFFICE _____

E-MAIL _____ FAX _____

HOLIDAY GREETINGS		
Year	Sent	Rec

NAME _____

ADDRESS _____

CITY/STATE/ZIP _____

HOME _____ OFFICE _____

E-MAIL _____ FAX _____

HOLIDAY GREETINGS		
Year	Sent	Rec

NAME _____

ADDRESS _____

CITY/STATE/ZIP _____

HOME _____ OFFICE _____

E-MAIL _____ FAX _____

HOLIDAY GREETINGS		
Year	Sent	Rec

Havasu Falls
KERRICK JAMES

A

B

C

D

EF

G

H

IJ

K

L

M

N

O

PQ

R

S

T

	HOLIDAY GREETINGS		
	Year	Sent	Rec

NAME _____

ADDRESS _____

CITY/STATE/ZIP _____

HOME _____OFFICE _____

E-MAIL _____FAX _____

	HOLIDAY GREETINGS		
	Year	Sent	Rec

NAME _____

ADDRESS _____

CITY/STATE/ZIP _____

HOME _____OFFICE _____

E-MAIL _____FAX _____

	HOLIDAY GREETINGS		
	Year	Sent	Rec

NAME _____

ADDRESS _____

CITY/STATE/ZIP _____

HOME _____OFFICE _____

E-MAIL _____FAX _____

	HOLIDAY GREETINGS		
	Year	Sent	Rec

NAME _____

ADDRESS _____

CITY/STATE/ZIP _____

HOME _____OFFICE _____

E-MAIL _____FAX _____

	HOLIDAY GREETINGS		
	Year	Sent	Rec

NAME _____

ADDRESS _____

CITY/STATE/ZIP _____

HOME _____OFFICE _____

E-MAIL _____FAX _____

NAME _____

ADDRESS _____

CITY/STATE/ZIP _____

HOME _____OFFICE _____

E-MAIL _____FAX _____

HOLIDAY GREETINGS		
Year	Sent	Rec

NAME _____

ADDRESS _____

CITY/STATE/ZIP _____

HOME _____OFFICE _____

E-MAIL _____FAX _____

HOLIDAY GREETINGS		
Year	Sent	Rec

NAME _____

ADDRESS _____

CITY/STATE/ZIP _____

HOME _____OFFICE _____

E-MAIL _____FAX _____

HOLIDAY GREETINGS		
Year	Sent	Rec

NAME _____

ADDRESS _____

CITY/STATE/ZIP _____

HOME _____OFFICE _____

E-MAIL _____FAX _____

HOLIDAY GREETINGS		
Year	Sent	Rec

NAME _____

ADDRESS _____

CITY/STATE/ZIP _____

HOME _____OFFICE _____

E-MAIL _____FAX _____

HOLIDAY GREETINGS		
Year	Sent	Rec

	HOLIDAY GREETINGS		
	Year	Sent	Rec

NAME _____

ADDRESS _____

CITY/STATE/ZIP _____

HOME _____ OFFICE _____

E-MAIL _____ FAX _____

	HOLIDAY GREETINGS		
	Year	Sent	Rec

NAME _____

ADDRESS _____

CITY/STATE/ZIP _____

HOME _____ OFFICE _____

E-MAIL _____ FAX _____

	HOLIDAY GREETINGS		
	Year	Sent	Rec

NAME _____

ADDRESS _____

CITY/STATE/ZIP _____

HOME _____ OFFICE _____

E-MAIL _____ FAX _____

	HOLIDAY GREETINGS		
	Year	Sent	Rec

NAME _____

ADDRESS _____

CITY/STATE/ZIP _____

HOME _____ OFFICE _____

E-MAIL _____ FAX _____

	HOLIDAY GREETINGS		
	Year	Sent	Rec

NAME _____

ADDRESS _____

CITY/STATE/ZIP _____

HOME _____ OFFICE _____

E-MAIL _____ FAX _____

NAME _____

ADDRESS _____

CITY/STATE/ZIP _____

HOME _____ OFFICE _____

E-MAIL _____ FAX _____

HOLIDAY GREETINGS		
Year	Sent	Rec

NAME _____

ADDRESS _____

CITY/STATE/ZIP _____

HOME _____ OFFICE _____

E-MAIL _____ FAX _____

HOLIDAY GREETINGS		
Year	Sent	Rec

NAME _____

ADDRESS _____

CITY/STATE/ZIP _____

HOME _____ OFFICE _____

E-MAIL _____ FAX _____

HOLIDAY GREETINGS		
Year	Sent	Rec

NAME _____

ADDRESS _____

CITY/STATE/ZIP _____

HOME _____ OFFICE _____

E-MAIL _____ FAX _____

HOLIDAY GREETINGS		
Year	Sent	Rec

NAME _____

ADDRESS _____

CITY/STATE/ZIP _____

HOME _____ OFFICE _____

E-MAIL _____ FAX _____

HOLIDAY GREETINGS		
Year	Sent	Rec

NAME _____

ADDRESS _____

CITY/STATE/ZIP _____

HOME _____ OFFICE _____

E-MAIL _____ FAX _____

HOLIDAY GREETINGS		
Year	Sent	Rec

NAME _____

ADDRESS _____

CITY/STATE/ZIP _____

HOME _____ OFFICE _____

E-MAIL _____ FAX _____

HOLIDAY GREETINGS		
Year	Sent	Rec

NAME _____

ADDRESS _____

CITY/STATE/ZIP _____

HOME _____ OFFICE _____

E-MAIL _____ FAX _____

HOLIDAY GREETINGS		
Year	Sent	Rec

NAME _____

ADDRESS _____

CITY/STATE/ZIP _____

HOME _____ OFFICE _____

E-MAIL _____ FAX _____

HOLIDAY GREETINGS		
Year	Sent	Rec

NAME _____

ADDRESS _____

CITY/STATE/ZIP _____

HOME _____ OFFICE _____

E-MAIL _____ FAX _____

HOLIDAY GREETINGS		
Year	Sent	Rec

NAME _____

ADDRESS _____

CITY/STATE/ZIP _____

HOME _____OFFICE _____

E-MAIL _____FAX _____

HOLIDAY GREETINGS		
Year	Sent	Rec

NAME _____

ADDRESS _____

CITY/STATE/ZIP _____

HOME _____OFFICE _____

E-MAIL _____FAX _____

HOLIDAY GREETINGS		
Year	Sent	Rec

NAME _____

ADDRESS _____

CITY/STATE/ZIP _____

HOME _____OFFICE _____

E-MAIL _____FAX _____

HOLIDAY GREETINGS		
Year	Sent	Rec

NAME _____

ADDRESS _____

CITY/STATE/ZIP _____

HOME _____OFFICE _____

E-MAIL _____FAX _____

HOLIDAY GREETINGS		
Year	Sent	Rec

NAME _____

ADDRESS _____

CITY/STATE/ZIP _____

HOME _____OFFICE _____

E-MAIL _____FAX _____

HOLIDAY GREETINGS		
Year	Sent	Rec

East Clear Creek
RICHARD STRANGE

UV

A

B

C

D

EF

G

H

IJ

K

L

M

N

O

PQ

R

S

T

UV

NAME _____

ADDRESS _____

CITY/STATE/ZIP _____

HOME _____ OFFICE _____

E-MAIL _____ FAX _____

HOLIDAY GREETINGS		
Year	Sent	Rec

NAME _____

ADDRESS _____

CITY/STATE/ZIP _____

HOME _____ OFFICE _____

E-MAIL _____ FAX _____

HOLIDAY GREETINGS		
Year	Sent	Rec

NAME _____

ADDRESS _____

CITY/STATE/ZIP _____

HOME _____ OFFICE _____

E-MAIL _____ FAX _____

HOLIDAY GREETINGS		
Year	Sent	Rec

NAME _____

ADDRESS _____

CITY/STATE/ZIP _____

HOME _____ OFFICE _____

E-MAIL _____ FAX _____

HOLIDAY GREETINGS		
Year	Sent	Rec

NAME _____

ADDRESS _____

CITY/STATE/ZIP _____

HOME _____ OFFICE _____

E-MAIL _____ FAX _____

HOLIDAY GREETINGS		
Year	Sent	Rec

HOLIDAY GREETINGS		
Year	Sent	Rec

NAME _____

ADDRESS _____

CITY/STATE/ZIP _____

HOME _____OFFICE _____

E-MAIL _____FAX _____

HOLIDAY GREETINGS		
Year	Sent	Rec

NAME _____

ADDRESS _____

CITY/STATE/ZIP _____

HOME _____OFFICE _____

E-MAIL _____FAX _____

HOLIDAY GREETINGS		
Year	Sent	Rec

NAME _____

ADDRESS _____

CITY/STATE/ZIP _____

HOME _____OFFICE _____

E-MAIL _____FAX _____

HOLIDAY GREETINGS		
Year	Sent	Rec

NAME _____

ADDRESS _____

CITY/STATE/ZIP _____

HOME _____OFFICE _____

E-MAIL _____FAX _____

HOLIDAY GREETINGS		
Year	Sent	Rec

NAME _____

ADDRESS _____

CITY/STATE/ZIP _____

HOME _____OFFICE _____

E-MAIL _____FAX _____

NAME _____	HOLIDAY GREETINGS		
	Year	Sent	Rec
ADDRESS _____			
CITY/STATE/ZIP _____			
HOME _____OFFICE _____			
E-MAIL _____FAX _____			

NAME _____	HOLIDAY GREETINGS		
	Year	Sent	Rec
ADDRESS _____			
CITY/STATE/ZIP _____			
HOME _____OFFICE _____			
E-MAIL _____FAX _____			

NAME _____	HOLIDAY GREETINGS		
	Year	Sent	Rec
ADDRESS _____			
CITY/STATE/ZIP _____			
HOME _____OFFICE _____			
E-MAIL _____FAX _____			

NAME _____	HOLIDAY GREETINGS		
	Year	Sent	Rec
ADDRESS _____			
CITY/STATE/ZIP _____			
HOME _____OFFICE _____			
E-MAIL _____FAX _____			

NAME _____	HOLIDAY GREETINGS		
	Year	Sent	Rec
ADDRESS _____			
CITY/STATE/ZIP _____			
HOME _____OFFICE _____			
E-MAIL _____FAX _____			

NAME _____

ADDRESS _____

CITY/STATE/ZIP _____

HOME _____ OFFICE _____

E-MAIL _____ FAX _____

HOLIDAY GREETINGS		
Year	Sent	Rec

NAME _____

ADDRESS _____

CITY/STATE/ZIP _____

HOME _____ OFFICE _____

E-MAIL _____ FAX _____

HOLIDAY GREETINGS		
Year	Sent	Rec

NAME _____

ADDRESS _____

CITY/STATE/ZIP _____

HOME _____ OFFICE _____

E-MAIL _____ FAX _____

HOLIDAY GREETINGS		
Year	Sent	Rec

NAME _____

ADDRESS _____

CITY/STATE/ZIP _____

HOME _____ OFFICE _____

E-MAIL _____ FAX _____

HOLIDAY GREETINGS		
Year	Sent	Rec

NAME _____

ADDRESS _____

CITY/STATE/ZIP _____

HOME _____ OFFICE _____

E-MAIL _____ FAX _____

HOLIDAY GREETINGS		
Year	Sent	Rec

NAME _____

ADDRESS _____

CITY/STATE/ZIP _____

HOME _____ OFFICE _____

E-MAIL _____ FAX _____

HOLIDAY GREETINGS		
Year	Sent	Rec

NAME _____

ADDRESS _____

CITY/STATE/ZIP _____

HOME _____ OFFICE _____

E-MAIL _____ FAX _____

HOLIDAY GREETINGS		
Year	Sent	Rec

NAME _____

ADDRESS _____

CITY/STATE/ZIP _____

HOME _____ OFFICE _____

E-MAIL _____ FAX _____

HOLIDAY GREETINGS		
Year	Sent	Rec

NAME _____

ADDRESS _____

CITY/STATE/ZIP _____

HOME _____ OFFICE _____

E-MAIL _____ FAX _____

HOLIDAY GREETINGS		
Year	Sent	Rec

NAME _____

ADDRESS _____

CITY/STATE/ZIP _____

HOME _____ OFFICE _____

E-MAIL _____ FAX _____

HOLIDAY GREETINGS		
Year	Sent	Rec

NAME _____

ADDRESS _____

CITY/STATE/ZIP _____

HOME _____OFFICE _____

E-MAIL _____FAX _____

HOLIDAY GREETINGS		
Year	Sent	Rec

NAME _____

ADDRESS _____

CITY/STATE/ZIP _____

HOME _____OFFICE _____

E-MAIL _____FAX _____

HOLIDAY GREETINGS		
Year	Sent	Rec

NAME _____

ADDRESS _____

CITY/STATE/ZIP _____

HOME _____OFFICE _____

E-MAIL _____FAX _____

HOLIDAY GREETINGS		
Year	Sent	Rec

NAME _____

ADDRESS _____

CITY/STATE/ZIP _____

HOME _____OFFICE _____

E-MAIL _____FAX _____

HOLIDAY GREETINGS		
Year	Sent	Rec

NAME _____

ADDRESS _____

CITY/STATE/ZIP _____

HOME _____OFFICE _____

E-MAIL _____FAX _____

HOLIDAY GREETINGS		
Year	Sent	Rec

Spider Rock, Canyon de Chelly
STEPHEN CHERNEK

A

B

C

D

EF

G

H

IJ

K

L

M

N

O

PQ

R

S

T

UV

WX

HOLIDAY GREETINGS		
Year	Sent	Rec

NAME _____

ADDRESS _____

CITY/STATE/ZIP _____

HOME _____ OFFICE _____

E-MAIL _____ FAX _____

HOLIDAY GREETINGS		
Year	Sent	Rec

NAME _____

ADDRESS _____

CITY/STATE/ZIP _____

HOME _____ OFFICE _____

E-MAIL _____ FAX _____

HOLIDAY GREETINGS		
Year	Sent	Rec

NAME _____

ADDRESS _____

CITY/STATE/ZIP _____

HOME _____ OFFICE _____

E-MAIL _____ FAX _____

HOLIDAY GREETINGS		
Year	Sent	Rec

NAME _____

ADDRESS _____

CITY/STATE/ZIP _____

HOME _____ OFFICE _____

E-MAIL _____ FAX _____

HOLIDAY GREETINGS		
Year	Sent	Rec

NAME _____

ADDRESS _____

CITY/STATE/ZIP _____

HOME _____ OFFICE _____

E-MAIL _____ FAX _____

NAME _____

ADDRESS _____

CITY/STATE/ZIP _____

HOME _____OFFICE _____

E-MAIL _____FAX _____

HOLIDAY GREETINGS		
Year	Sent	Rec

NAME _____

ADDRESS _____

CITY/STATE/ZIP _____

HOME _____OFFICE _____

E-MAIL _____FAX _____

HOLIDAY GREETINGS		
Year	Sent	Rec

NAME _____

ADDRESS _____

CITY/STATE/ZIP _____

HOME _____OFFICE _____

E-MAIL _____FAX _____

HOLIDAY GREETINGS		
Year	Sent	Rec

NAME _____

ADDRESS _____

CITY/STATE/ZIP _____

HOME _____OFFICE _____

E-MAIL _____FAX _____

HOLIDAY GREETINGS		
Year	Sent	Rec

NAME _____

ADDRESS _____

CITY/STATE/ZIP _____

HOME _____OFFICE _____

E-MAIL _____FAX _____

HOLIDAY GREETINGS		
Year	Sent	Rec

NAME _____

ADDRESS _____

CITY/STATE/ZIP _____

HOME _____ OFFICE _____

E-MAIL _____ FAX _____

HOLIDAY GREETINGS		
Year	Sent	Rec

NAME _____

ADDRESS _____

CITY/STATE/ZIP _____

HOME _____ OFFICE _____

E-MAIL _____ FAX _____

HOLIDAY GREETINGS		
Year	Sent	Rec

NAME _____

ADDRESS _____

CITY/STATE/ZIP _____

HOME _____ OFFICE _____

E-MAIL _____ FAX _____

HOLIDAY GREETINGS		
Year	Sent	Rec

NAME _____

ADDRESS _____

CITY/STATE/ZIP _____

HOME _____ OFFICE _____

E-MAIL _____ FAX _____

HOLIDAY GREETINGS		
Year	Sent	Rec

NAME _____

ADDRESS _____

CITY/STATE/ZIP _____

HOME _____ OFFICE _____

E-MAIL _____ FAX _____

HOLIDAY GREETINGS		
Year	Sent	Rec

HOLIDAY GREETINGS			
Year	Sent	Rec	

NAME _____

ADDRESS _____

CITY/STATE/ZIP _____

HOME _____ OFFICE _____

E-MAIL _____ FAX _____

HOLIDAY GREETINGS			
Year	Sent	Rec	

NAME _____

ADDRESS _____

CITY/STATE/ZIP _____

HOME _____ OFFICE _____

E-MAIL _____ FAX _____

HOLIDAY GREETINGS			
Year	Sent	Rec	

NAME _____

ADDRESS _____

CITY/STATE/ZIP _____

HOME _____ OFFICE _____

E-MAIL _____ FAX _____

HOLIDAY GREETINGS			
Year	Sent	Rec	

NAME _____

ADDRESS _____

CITY/STATE/ZIP _____

HOME _____ OFFICE _____

E-MAIL _____ FAX _____

HOLIDAY GREETINGS			
Year	Sent	Rec	

NAME _____

ADDRESS _____

CITY/STATE/ZIP _____

HOME _____ OFFICE _____

E-MAIL _____ FAX _____

NAME _____

HOLIDAY GREETINGS		
Year	Sent	Rec

ADDRESS _____

CITY/STATE/ZIP _____

HOME _____OFFICE _____

E-MAIL _____FAX _____

NAME _____

HOLIDAY GREETINGS		
Year	Sent	Rec

ADDRESS _____

CITY/STATE/ZIP _____

HOME _____OFFICE _____

E-MAIL _____FAX _____

NAME _____

HOLIDAY GREETINGS		
Year	Sent	Rec

ADDRESS _____

CITY/STATE/ZIP _____

HOME _____OFFICE _____

E-MAIL _____FAX _____

NAME _____

HOLIDAY GREETINGS		
Year	Sent	Rec

ADDRESS _____

CITY/STATE/ZIP _____

HOME _____OFFICE _____

E-MAIL _____FAX _____

NAME _____

HOLIDAY GREETINGS		
Year	Sent	Rec

ADDRESS _____

CITY/STATE/ZIP _____

HOME _____OFFICE _____

E-MAIL _____FAX _____

NAME _____

ADDRESS _____

CITY/STATE/ZIP _____

HOME _____ OFFICE _____

E-MAIL _____ FAX _____

HOLIDAY GREETINGS		
Year	Sent	Rec

NAME _____

ADDRESS _____

CITY/STATE/ZIP _____

HOME _____ OFFICE _____

E-MAIL _____ FAX _____

HOLIDAY GREETINGS		
Year	Sent	Rec

NAME _____

ADDRESS _____

CITY/STATE/ZIP _____

HOME _____ OFFICE _____

E-MAIL _____ FAX _____

HOLIDAY GREETINGS		
Year	Sent	Rec

NAME _____

ADDRESS _____

CITY/STATE/ZIP _____

HOME _____ OFFICE _____

E-MAIL _____ FAX _____

HOLIDAY GREETINGS		
Year	Sent	Rec

NAME _____

ADDRESS _____

CITY/STATE/ZIP _____

HOME _____ OFFICE _____

E-MAIL _____ FAX _____

HOLIDAY GREETINGS		
Year	Sent	Rec

Slot Canyon near Page
MICHAEL FATALI

A

B

C

D

EF

G

H

IJ

K

L

M

N

O

PQ

R

S

T

UV

WX

YZ

HOLIDAY GREETINGS

Year	Sent	Rec

NAME

ADDRESS

CITY/STATE/ZIP

HOME _____ OFFICE

E-MAIL _____ FAX

HOLIDAY GREETINGS

Year	Sent	Rec

NAME

ADDRESS

CITY/STATE/ZIP

HOME _____ OFFICE

E-MAIL _____ FAX

HOLIDAY GREETINGS

Year	Sent	Rec

NAME

ADDRESS

CITY/STATE/ZIP

HOME _____ OFFICE

E-MAIL _____ FAX

HOLIDAY GREETINGS

Year	Sent	Rec

NAME

ADDRESS

CITY/STATE/ZIP

HOME _____ OFFICE

E-MAIL _____ FAX

HOLIDAY GREETINGS

Year	Sent	Rec

NAME

ADDRESS

CITY/STATE/ZIP

HOME _____ OFFICE

E-MAIL _____ FAX

HOLIDAY
GREETINGS

Year	Sent	Rec

NAME _____

ADDRESS _____

CITY/STATE/ZIP _____

HOME _____ OFFICE _____

E-MAIL _____ FAX _____

HOLIDAY
GREETINGS

Year	Sent	Rec

NAME _____

ADDRESS _____

CITY/STATE/ZIP _____

HOME _____ OFFICE _____

E-MAIL _____ FAX _____

HOLIDAY
GREETINGS

Year	Sent	Rec

NAME _____

ADDRESS _____

CITY/STATE/ZIP _____

HOME _____ OFFICE _____

E-MAIL _____ FAX _____

HOLIDAY
GREETINGS

Year	Sent	Rec

NAME _____

ADDRESS _____

CITY/STATE/ZIP _____

HOME _____ OFFICE _____

E-MAIL _____ FAX _____

HOLIDAY
GREETINGS

Year	Sent	Rec

NAME _____

ADDRESS _____

CITY/STATE/ZIP _____

HOME _____ OFFICE _____

E-MAIL _____ FAX _____

HOLIDAY GREETINGS		
Year	Sent	Rec

NAME _____

ADDRESS _____

CITY/STATE/ZIP _____

HOME _____ OFFICE _____

E-MAIL _____ FAX _____

HOLIDAY GREETINGS		
Year	Sent	Rec

NAME _____

ADDRESS _____

CITY/STATE/ZIP _____

HOME _____ OFFICE _____

E-MAIL _____ FAX _____

HOLIDAY GREETINGS		
Year	Sent	Rec

NAME _____

ADDRESS _____

CITY/STATE/ZIP _____

HOME _____ OFFICE _____

E-MAIL _____ FAX _____

HOLIDAY GREETINGS		
Year	Sent	Rec

NAME _____

ADDRESS _____

CITY/STATE/ZIP _____

HOME _____ OFFICE _____

E-MAIL _____ FAX _____

HOLIDAY GREETINGS		
Year	Sent	Rec

NAME _____

ADDRESS _____

CITY/STATE/ZIP _____

HOME _____ OFFICE _____

E-MAIL _____ FAX _____

HOLIDAY GREETINGS

Year	Sent	Rec

NAME

ADDRESS

CITY/STATE/ZIP

HOME   OFFICE

E-MAIL   FAX

HOLIDAY GREETINGS

Year	Sent	Rec

NAME

ADDRESS

CITY/STATE/ZIP

HOME   OFFICE

E-MAIL   FAX

HOLIDAY GREETINGS

Year	Sent	Rec

NAME

ADDRESS

CITY/STATE/ZIP

HOME   OFFICE

E-MAIL   FAX

HOLIDAY GREETINGS

Year	Sent	Rec

NAME

ADDRESS

CITY/STATE/ZIP

HOME   OFFICE

E-MAIL   FAX

HOLIDAY GREETINGS

Year	Sent	Rec

NAME

ADDRESS

CITY/STATE/ZIP

HOME   OFFICE

E-MAIL   FAX

HOLIDAY GREETINGS		
Year	Sent	Rec

NAME _____

ADDRESS _____

CITY/STATE/ZIP _____

HOME _____ OFFICE _____

E-MAIL _____ FAX _____

HOLIDAY GREETINGS		
Year	Sent	Rec

NAME _____

ADDRESS _____

CITY/STATE/ZIP _____

HOME _____ OFFICE _____

E-MAIL _____ FAX _____

HOLIDAY GREETINGS		
Year	Sent	Rec

NAME _____

ADDRESS _____

CITY/STATE/ZIP _____

HOME _____ OFFICE _____

E-MAIL _____ FAX _____

HOLIDAY GREETINGS		
Year	Sent	Rec

NAME _____

ADDRESS _____

CITY/STATE/ZIP _____

HOME _____ OFFICE _____

E-MAIL _____ FAX _____

HOLIDAY GREETINGS		
Year	Sent	Rec

NAME _____

ADDRESS _____

CITY/STATE/ZIP _____

HOME _____ OFFICE _____

E-MAIL _____ FAX _____

HOLIDAY GREETINGS — Year / Sent / Rec

NAME _____

ADDRESS _____

CITY/STATE/ZIP _____

HOME _____ OFFICE _____

E-MAIL _____ FAX _____

HOLIDAY GREETINGS — Year / Sent / Rec

NAME _____

ADDRESS _____

CITY/STATE/ZIP _____

HOME _____ OFFICE _____

E-MAIL _____ FAX _____

HOLIDAY GREETINGS — Year / Sent / Rec

NAME _____

ADDRESS _____

CITY/STATE/ZIP _____

HOME _____ OFFICE _____

E-MAIL _____ FAX _____

HOLIDAY GREETINGS — Year / Sent / Rec

NAME _____

ADDRESS _____

CITY/STATE/ZIP _____

HOME _____ OFFICE _____

E-MAIL _____ FAX _____

HOLIDAY GREETINGS — Year / Sent / Rec

NAME _____

ADDRESS _____

CITY/STATE/ZIP _____

HOME _____ OFFICE _____

E-MAIL _____ FAX _____

Dates to remember

Dates to remember

_____   _____
_____   _____
_____   _____
_____   _____
_____   _____
_____   _____
_____   _____
_____   _____
_____   _____
_____   _____
_____   _____
_____   _____
_____   _____
_____   _____
_____   _____
_____   _____
_____   _____
_____   _____
_____   _____
_____   _____
_____   _____
_____   _____
_____   _____
_____   _____
_____   _____

_____   _____
_____   _____
_____   _____
_____   _____
_____   _____
_____   _____
_____   _____
_____   _____
_____   _____
_____   _____
_____   _____
_____   _____
_____   _____
_____   _____
_____   _____
_____   _____
_____   _____
_____   _____
_____   _____
_____   _____
_____   _____
_____   _____
_____   _____
_____   _____
_____   _____
_____   _____

Frequently called numbers